SAVE YOURSELF: A Practical Guide to Understanding Emotions, Energy and Health.

Published by AUDVER BOOKS. In association with 1008 Solutions.
P.O. Box 156
Hot Springs, SD 57747

ISBN: 0-9661825-9-6

Cover Design by Ebun Adelona in conjunction with David Matthew Bey
Graphic Art by David Matthew Olatunji Bey
Illustrations by Shukuru Copland-Sanders and David Matthew Bey
Interior Editing by Nefetiti Myrick

1. Health Promotion
2. Self-Help
3. Chakras
Soft Cover
$14.95

SAVE YOURSELF:

A Practical Guide for Understanding Energy, Emotions and Health

by

Ebun L. Adelona Ph.D.

To Contact the Author

Ebun Adelona is available for Quantum Dynamic's Transformation Breath Seminars and a variety of Life Workshops. The author would also appreciate hearing from you, and receiving information about your response to the book and how it has assisted you.
We cannot guarantee that every letter received by the author will be answered but please feel free to write to:

Ebun Adelona
P.O. Box 156
Hot Springs, SD 57747

or

E-mail ade1008@gwtc.net

This book is dedicated to God, Wanka Tanka,
Oludumare, and
Divine Mother the Creator of all things;
to the Supreme Reality personified Shri Shri
1008 Shri Bhagwan Herakhan Wale Baba
affectionately known as "Babaji"; and to the
Orisha Awo (Mysteries of Nature) that guide my
consciousness Yemoja/Olokun.

Contents

Acknowledgments

I thank my daughter N'Zinga and granddaughter Ife who shared the journey of developing this book with me and patiently endured when I was busy writing.

I thank Kali who initiated me into Quantum Dynamics, Laura Morning Star who taught me how to conduct a seminar and Jim Dvorak who initiated me as a teacher of Quantum Dynamics.

I thank the core members of the Quantum Dynamics Support group Ajeley, Brinda, Carole, Deborah, Denise, Diane, Geraldine, Kamal, Kathy, Lindsay, Marilyn, Peggy, Stacey, Susan, Vetora, Xenia, and Zakiyah. Whose encouragement and loving feedback has supported me in writing this book.

I thank my clients who have shared their issues with me and trusted the process to assist them in their transformation.

I thank all those who have participated in the Quantum Dynamic's Transformation Breath Seminars and inspired me to share this information by their examples of change and growth.

I thank my Iyaorisha, Iyanla Vanzant, for the opportunity to teach and learn at the Inner Visions Institute for Spiritual Development. Her dedication to sharing spiritual principles and generous sharing of her experiences as a author has inspired me share these ideas about healing that God has given me.

I thank Colleen who deepened my understanding of the power of Breath though Rebirthing and strengthened my connection to "Babaji" with weekly Aarti and her yearly pilgrimages to Haidakhandi.

I thank the divine messengers of God, cleverly disguised as the FBI, who set me on a conscious spiritual journey and the divine teachers who showed up in accord with my vision to guide me. Lisa who taught me to chant, Daya who taught me nutrition and colon cleansing, Pagmini who taught me to fast, Morning Star who introduced me to Lakota ceremony.

I thank my readers Ayisha Davis, Adara Walton, Fu Weems, Marianne Rothschild MD., Leslie Grey, and Susan Shorter.

I thank Almasi Wilcox for coining the phrase "Save Yourself" used as the title of this book.

I thank my sister Adryian Dasheil and my friends Stephanie Steele, Earthy Spaulding, and Shukuru Copeland Sanders, who have motivated me with their inquiries "Where's the book?"

I thank Adara and Fu for their continued encouragement and support.

I thank the divine Angel, Neffitti who has masterfully edited this book and kept me on task with her presence.

Introduction

It was morning, the week of my fortieth birthday I got up, and suddenly, I knew that this life was not what I wanted. I was an activist, a revolutionary, a dynamic speaker for the rights of people in Harlem to have wellness, to choose their health care. I was in the midst of a struggle to prevent the closure of Sydenham hospital. Struggle was my life. Yes, that was my mantra. Indeed, struggle was what my life had become. But struggle was not joyful, and it was not happiness. It was hard work and sacrifice with satisfaction when I was able to keep a clinic open or assist a community group with developing a program. I felt most alive when engaged in health activism. How could I possibly let that go? I didn't have a clue about how to change my life but that didn't matter. God did, and soon my life would be totally turned around.

Two weeks later in the early hours of the morning of April 19, 1980, I awoke to the sounds of my front door crashing in and a male voice shouting, "Come out with your hands up." Well, I thought, robbers don't tell you to come out with your hands up. It must be the cops! So, I got out of bed, put on a pajama jumpsuit, and as I entered my L -shaped hallway I thought, better come out all at once or you'll get shot. I stepped around the corner into a brilliant spotlight and faced two rows of white men in black jackets and pants with FBI stenciled across their chests in large fluorescent letters. One row knelt and the other stood with their guns in firing positions aimed at me. I could feel their excitement and fear. All I could think was -They are scared; let me tell them that my five year old daughter is in the room behind them because if they freak, we're dead.

That night was a turning point in my life. I subsequently held a press conference and engaged lawyers to file a lawsuit against the F.B.I. We ultimately settled the lawsuit out of court The reason for the raid, gleaned from the deposition documents, was that they thought I was Assata Shakur, leader of the Black Liberation Army.

The chaos that erupted in my life following the FBI raid, of over 50 agents on 92 Morningside Ave,. and the subsequent lawsuit, was a divine opportunity for change. I was a trained nurse psychotherapist. I had undergone individual and group therapy and thought I was aware of my issues and in control. Yet, I was not prepared for the flood of thoughts, feelings, and experiences that were immediately released after that fateful night which sent me plunging me into a daily search for meaning in my life. In the ensuing weeks I could not live with the pain. I challenged God to give me guidance or end my life. Not having received an answer at the end of a month I stopped eating and drinking.

On the seventh day of this fast I had a vision: guidance was promised me in the form of a series of teachers with specific signs to let me know they were the promised ones. I learned from my first teacher how to chant. My second teacher taught me about eating vegan and colon cleansing.. Each of these modalities assisted me to calm my thoughts, ground my self, and experience less pain.

Despite all that I learned and did to control my thoughts and ease my pain, I couldn't fully release the upsetting feelings nor totally stop the self abusive thoughts nor rise above the repetitious painful experiences. Somehow this incident had opened up the flood gates releasing everything I had ever repressed, suppressed or denied. It was as if every hurt, insecurity, embarrassment, and injury was happening all over again

2

every day, simultaneously. Suicide was only 24 hours away! Everyday I awoke and made a promise that today I would not kill myself. I lived one day at a time for a year. I could never commit to anything for more than twenty four hours, because I didn't know what torrential flood of thoughts, feelings or experiences, from which I couldn't save myself, might overwhelm me from day to day. Perhaps taking my life would be the only way to stop the torment of each surfacing.

My day of deliverance began with a phone call from a friend. An acquaintance of hers was coming to New York to conduct a workshop on a technique called Quantum Dynamics. Since I had an established client base and access to other practitioners with a client base, my friend wanted me to assist her with publicizing the workshops. I agreed and requested some literature about the technique. The next week a small booklet arrived, entitled *Quantum Dynamics: Productive Conversion of Mass to Energy* by Jim Dvorak. I began reading it primarily with the intent of finding what I needed to extract to create a workshop flyer. But as I read I saw a process being laid out that was the answer to my torment - the ability to release the feelings, clear the thoughts and change the experiences. I was ecstatic and told my friend all I wanted in exchange for my publicity work was to attend the workshop.

In the workshop, I learned about Chakras and core beliefs that block the energy within these energy centers. I learned that my thoughts were creative and learned to process myself, which allowed me to release upsetting feelings and abusive thoughts in 10 seconds or less. I wanted to be able to use this technique called Quantum Dynamics. And use it I did. I cleared more issues in a year of working with Quantum Dynamics than I had in seven years of therapy. I was no longer a passive victim of torrential feelings and thoughts bound to a repetitious pattern of experiences that I was hopelessly unable to change. Yes, my odyssey had ended. I could save myself. Friends remarked how much lighter, happier, and younger I appeared.

I wanted to share this empowerment with others. When a Quantum Dynamics teacher, promised me by Spirit, visited the New York area, I attached myself to her and shepherded people to her workshops. Finally, after a year of watching clients and friends benefit from Quantum Dynamics, I wanted to be able to teach it. I contacted Jim Dvorak, who in a meditative state received this tool to reintroduce to the planet, completed the training, and for twenty years initiated and taught Quantum Dynamics to people. Now it is time to share the knowledge with a larger audience. This is why I am writing this practical guide to understanding energy, emotions and health based on observations and insights gleaned from my personal and professional work with Quantum Dynamics over the past twenty one years.

Using the Book

We are so much more than a physical body, and when we limit our view of ourselves to the physical we are limiting our divine birth right, our connection to our creator, and our ability to heal and transform ourselves. Chakras are the energy centers for that connection, for that healing and for that transformation. When I first began to work with Quantum Dynamics, the focus was on seven Chakras. We are now in a new millennium and our view has expanded to include eleven Chakras. This book, therefore, discusses the seven Chakras anchored in the physical body, the four Chakras outside the physical body and the front and backside of all eleven Chakras. The latter four out of body Chakras are seldom discussed but are none the less important because of the role they play in linking the visible realms of existence with the invisible realms of existence.

This book is for people who have no exposure to those who have basic to intermediary understanding of energy and Chakras. Drawing from multiple sources, it is a text intended to explain the Body as an integrated system designed to maintain perfect heath. It is not intended to replace or substitute for the services of a qualified physician. Throughout the text, I will use capitalized Body when referring to the physical body as well as the three energy bodies, and non capitalized body when referring only to the physical body. The first chapter gives an overview of the Body as an energy system. The second chapter covers basic information about each of the eleven Chakras: their location, spokes, age of development, particular functions, spiritual goal; the judgement, thoughts, emotions, and physical manifestations experienced when the energy of a specific Chakra is blocked; and the healing element, musical note, breath, and related healing color. Following information about each Chakra, there is a Chakra story, which illustrates the proto typical behavior and belief for each of the eleven Chakras so that you may see how the Chakra functions and issues that show up in life. Use this information as you work with each individual Chakra in the fourth chapter. The third chapter discusses the purpose of the body; and the development of upset, separation, and disease. The fourth chapter is an eleven day guide, including exercises to experience and clear each Chakra. The addendum to the fourth chapter offers suggestions about foods to eat , colors to wear, and baths to use when clearing each Chakra. You may incorporate these suggestions into your first eleven day journey or use them as apart of a second eleven day journey. My suggestion is that if you have not worked with your Chakras before do not use this section initially.

I recommend that when you read chapters one through three, pay particular attention to the judgements, emotions, thoughts and physical manifestations of blocked energy and the Chakra stories which illustrate how these manifestations show up in life. Reflect on your life and consider how the judgements, emotions, thoughts and physical manifestations have appeared in your experiences. Which of the Chakra stories match patterns in your life. Read the summaries at the end of each chapter. These offer you an opportunity to absorb what you are reading. Take a few minutes to pause and reflect upon what you have read, note points that are especially relevant to your experience. Then prepare for your eleven day journey by beginning chapter four. At the end of the fourth chapter when you have completed the eleven day journey, you can begin the process again using the exercises over and over to reach additional levels of change. Once you have read and completed this book, continue to use it as a daily reference source for defining emotional, mental and spiritual components of issues you are encountering in your life. Use it to identify the master judgement underlying any physical, emotional, mental or spiritual issue. There is a reference list of books at the end of the book if you want to delve more deeply into the energy system you have discovered. You are encouraged to recommend or share this book with your physician or health care provider. This book is for you because you are ready to understand your life experiences and behaviors. You are ready to make another choice.

I am grateful to you for this opportunity to share. We are all related.

The North

We begin the journey in the North. The Northern energy takes our old ideas and freezes them, just as the rivers are frozen by the northern wind. Like the river, our ideas assume another form when they are thawed. This new form enables us to assimilate new ideas.

Chapter One
Unlimited Journey

*You are an energy being - an energy vessel. You have feelings
and e-motions (energy -in-motion) you cannot see, but
definitely experience . You are self contained but you affect and
impact everything around you, as the world does the same to
you.*
Adara L. Walton Every Body's Truth

Healing and transformation are the essentials to salvation.
Salvation is the restitution of wo/man to her/his spiritual
birthright. It embodies an inner overcoming, a change in
consciousness, transformation, in which we develop a
knowledge of God that frees us from all limitations. It
enables us to heal the sense of separation and awaken to
our true identity as an individualization of God. To heal is
to make happy. Healing is a process. It involves
recognizing that the life we are leading is not satisfying,
is not joyful; it involves believing that it is possible to
make a change; it involves recognizing that it is us who
needs to undo all that we have learned, not our parents, or
our husband or wife or our friends or coworkers; and,
finally, it involves making a commitment to change. In
recognizing that it is us that needs to change, we are now
open to receive information to assist us. It is our choice
how long the process takes and how painful it is.   It is
my experience that significant undoing can take place in
an instant, the "holy instant" as referred to in *A Course in
Miracles*. It is an instant of holiness, i.e., wholeness in
Spirit, mind and body, a consciousness of the all
pervading glory of God experienced for an instant. The

holy instant occurs as a result of us being willing and surrendering to the process. I've learned that the pain of undoing past learning is equal to the resistance we have to letting go once we recognize and commit to change. When we recognize and commit to change, we are in alignment with the natural processes of Life, of our essential being as a part of Life, of the planet and of the universe. The universe has conspired to support us in changing. We have stepped into the river and it will take us to its conclusion. When we step into the river, it is as the song says, "nothing stays the same, everything must change."

In our alignment with life, the information we receive and the lessons that we are offered are never more than we can handle at the time. Once we are in alignment, we can recognize every situation as a change opportunity. If we are working on anger, situation after situation will appear in which we will have the opportunity to choose a response other than anger. Our resistance to these opportunities to make a different choice engenders pain equal to the amount of resistance. But as the Borg say, "Resistance is futile."

Now hear me on this, I'm not saying that change does not involve discomfort, the discomfort of recognition. Re- cognition is when we identify something as previously seen, heard, felt, etc. When we recognate an experience, there is the discomfort of reliving that experience. The energy that was holding the experience is released and with it comes the flood of feelings previously denied. Yes, all of this brings forth discomfort during that period of undoing. But when we surrender and allow the release to take place, when we choose a different response, what a cleansing! And how much better we feel when it's over. We have healed an issue.

9

When we resist the process, it is painful because now, not only do we have the original experience's blocked energy, which is opening for release, we have the new experience with its energy, the judgement made about the new experience, and the energy blocked by that judgement . This is not an addition, i.e., previous experience plus new experience, it is a multiple. The current experience multiplied by the number of times that experience has occurred and not been undone. As a mathematical formula it would look like this: $CE \times (PE)_{100,000}$ {Current Experience x Previous Experience with the exponent $_{100,000}$ as the number of times that experience is used as a factor). That is why when processing people with Quantum Dynamics I ask about the number of times that experience has occured and release that exponent number. It takes more energy to suppress an experience ripe for undoing. Therefore, it is painful when the release is suppressed. Re-cognition is the first step in the process of healing.

Once you have decided to change by embarking upon the eleven day journey, let it flow like the river. Trust that nothing will come up that you can't handle and that you will always feel better after you have let go. And when you have let go, you're transformed. You will feel that shift in consciousness. Transformation brings about a change in your perspective. The situation which loomed so large, so mountainous in your life now has shrunk to the size of a pebble. It can be handled. You can see over it, under it, around it and you can throw it away. You begin to spontaneously experience joy bubbling up from within, love bubbling up from within, and you feel connected more and more frequently to others and to God.

Energy, Energy, Energy

In our everyday life, we are surrounded by energy, and we use it without giving much thought to it. We live in an energy ocean bombarded by energy waves! Want to see what's bombarding you? Turn your television dial to a non transmitting station and watch the screen. Those black and white dots are energy particles, protons and neutrons. Think about all the different kinds of energy we live with. Sun energy, moon energy, earth electromagnetic energy, gravitational energy, energy from electricity, the energy from colors, sounds, and the various types of energy used for communication devices - radio, television, cell phones to name just a few kinds of communication energy. These are all forms of unseen energy, different from each other, definately experienced. They are different because they have different vibratory frequencies, meaning that the energy particles move to and fro at different speeds, as in the case of the substance water. In the solid state when water is frozen, the molecules vibrate at a slower speed. In the liquid state, they vibrate faster so that water flows and as steam even faster creating a gaseous state in which water can barely be seen. This is an example of one substance having three different vibratory speeds, thus changing its appearance but not the fact that it is water. Vibratory rates can be different because they are different types of energy. For example, have you ever wondered why you don't get radio station programs on your television? Because they are two different kinds of energy waves. Radio waves are a band of the electro magnetic spectrum that can be used to transmit sound, vibrating at a particular frequency.

The transmitter of the radio station uses these frequencies to send out music, which your radio is specifically designed to receive. The waves of energy vibrating at that frequency, is the music you hear. Imagine, invisible energy becomes music! Television, on the other hand, uses light waves, which are turned into electric waves for transmission and then reconverted into visible light waves that form the pictures we see on our television set. Wonderful isn't it? Imagine, invisible energy becomes the Late Night Show. Two different forms of energy and two different types of receivers, a radio and a T.V.

Energy Body: Physical, Emotional, Mental, Spiritual

Our bodies are no less wondrous. We have one Body with four vibratory speeds. We have apparatus to receive and transmit different types of energy. If we accept invisible energy carrying music or images then why not accept invisible energy carrying Love, thought and emotions? The knowledge of accepting and understanding of our Body as energy is as important to the 21st century as the knowledge, understanding and acceptance of the world as round was to the 15 th century. Our Body vibrates at different speeds or rates, which is why the physical, emotional, mental, and spiritual aspect of our Body has different appearances. The physical body vibrates at a much slower rate than the emotional, mental and spiritual. The physical body is slowed down energy. That's why we are able to see the physical body because the energy patterns forming the components of the physical body vibrate at a rate so slow that it is opaque, i.e., does not allow light to pass through. It is therefore visible to our eyes and gives the appearance of solidity.

We mistakenly overlook the energies of the physical body because of this appearance of solidity, but these energies are measurable. Electrocardiograms, which measure the electrical energy of the heart, and electroencephalograms, which measure the electrical energy of the brain, are just two examples of instruments that have been developed to measure the energy of the physical body.

The other bodies, i.e., emotional, mental, and spiritual, that vibrate at faster rates, are not opaque and are invisible to most of us. The emotional body is experienced as waves of feeling. Most of us have experienced the emotional body when we experience a feeling sweeping over us. The emotional body is seen as color, which varies according to the emotion we feel. For example, contentment gives the emotional body a shimmering appearance. Emotion is energy accompanied by a specific thought. Thought sets energy-in-motion, and colors change as different emotions are activated. The mental body consists of strands of energy like a lattice work or web. The individual strands glow when thought occurs so that it looks like lightening. The color of the mental body varies from culture to culture because different cultures tap into differing points of Universal Consciousness .(Dale,144). When we are asleep, the back side of the mental body glows but the front side does not, it is dormant. The spiritual body appears as light. One layer of it is egg -shaped and iridescent, displaying a play of lustrous colors like those of the rainbow.

Those who see these bodies refer to them as the aura. "Aura is actually a Greek word that means 'breath,' or 'breeze.'Translating the Greek term into Latin, and you have *spiritus*, another word that also means 'wind' or 'breath' --specifically, the breath of god" (Bonheim,158).

The auric system is an energy field composed of eight basic fields beginning at the surface of the skin and extending out two to six feet from the physical body. Most books refer to these fields as layers, but in conceptualizing them as a system, layers have a static imagery, that undermines a full conceptualization of the interactive energy of this system. The auric system is an energy field moving in a figure eight pattern (Zhang) in which a vortex is created in those places where the figure eight intersects. A vortex whirls and draws. If you have ever watched water go down a drain you observe how the water whirls drawing more water down the drain. This whirling, drawing property of a vortex is what integrates the system. The integration of the Auric fields with the Chakras and the physical body is at the point where the figure eight crosses creating the energy vortex front side and back side. (See figure 1)

This point is an energy vortex. As a system, it is integrative, self regulating, communicative, adaptive, and exhibits equifinality. Integrative means it maintains coherence and integrity between the various energy frequencies of which it is comprised. It is self regulating because it maintains itself in mutual interactive wholeness, one aspect balancing or compensating for processes in another aspect of the system or within the same aspect of the system. Information is exchanged between subatomic particles of the physical body, with the organs, blood, lymph, and all tissues; between the four aspects of our Body; and between the Body and the energy of other people, the earth, sun, moon, God. This communicative information exchange maintains unity. Adaptive means that our Body changes in relation to what is going on within it and in relation to the ocean of energy in which we live. We are in a

Figure 1

Auric Field Figure Eight Energy Vortex

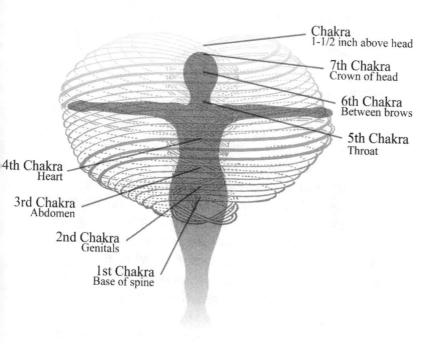

Chakra
1-1/2 inch above head

7th Chakra
Crown of head

6th Chakra
Between brows

5th Chakra
Throat

4th Chakra
Heart

3rd Chakra
Abdomen

2nd Chakra
Genitals

1st Chakra
Base of spine

constant state of change. Life is change and unity, which our Body expresses. Equifinality means that the final state may be reached from different initial conditions and in different ways. The final state of salvation can be reached regardless of who you are, what the circumstances of your life are or what you've done, and there are various ways of achieveing salvation.

The Auric Fields

This chapter discusses eight of the auric fields. In subsequent chapters, however, the fourth through eighth fields will be referred to as the spiritual body. The first auric field is the etheric body: this includes the skin and the energy field at the surface of the skin. The etheric field is an envelope surrounding every solid, liquid and gaseous particle of the physical body. It is an electro-magnetic and sonic medium. It distributes energy to the body and acts as a bridge between the physical body and the other Bodies. The etheric field is a subtle body of matter charged with the production of the type of physical body suited to that individualization of Universal Intelligence. In short, it is the template for the physical body through which God manifests creating a new life. The etheric matter for the infant body is taken from the body of the mother (A.E Powell, 68). While the potentialities of heredity are latent in the maternal ovum and the paternal spermatozoan, the selection in most instances is heavily influenced by the thoughts of the mother and the thoughts that are in interaction with her auric system. Remember, matter is slowed down energy, and thoughts are energy.

The etheric field is also referred to as the etheric double. The double can be separated from the physical body by accidents, death, anesthesia or projected by a trained expert. When separated, it appears as a second self; the experience of this separation may include seeing your physical body. There are accounts of people who have undergone anesthesia and recall floating and seeing their physical body laying upon the operating table. In my experience, it is a remembrance of being somewhere else, yet knowing that I was not dreaming and had not traveled there in the physical body. The first auric field is integrative, communicative and self regulating with the first Chakra at the base of the spine because their functions are linked. The etheric field manifests physical consciousness, and the first Chakra is concerned with having physical consciousness, survival and self preservation.

The second auric field is the emotional body. It connects internal feeling states with the people, events or experiences in which they are evoked or triggered . Feeling states are feelings unaccompanied by thoughts, judgements or beliefs. We are born experiencing two feelings --Love and Fear. Love and Fear are the only two feelings. Feelings fuel us, and Spirit flows as feeling. Love sustains, renews, heals and creates. Fear does the opposite. When a feeling is joined by a thought, judgement or belief, then emotions are produced and one experiences all the emotional gradations of which we are familiar, such as hate, resentment, anger, enthusiasm, contentment, happiness, etc. Emotions are energy-in motion accompanied by a thought.

The emotional body connects us to every person, event or experience that has evoked a feeling or created an emotion and carries away the waste products of those experiences. It also protects us from feelings and emotions that are not ours. A healthy emotional body enables us to differentiate between our feelings and emotions and those of others, maintain balance of our feelings, accept our feelings and emotions, and not hold onto emotions that enter us. The emotional body follows the contour of the physical body. The figure eight crosses at the second Chakra at the genital area. The emotional body is integrative, communicative, self regulating with the second Chakra because like the second Chakra it is concerned with passion and feelings.

The third auric field is the mental body. It is a weblike figure eight energy pattern which emanates primarily from the front and back side of the third Chakra in the genital area and follows the contour of the physical body. It is integrative, communicative and self regulating with the third Chakra which serves as our intellectual filter. The patterning of the energy web is unique to each of us and determined by our inherited and acquired intellectual abilities, educational experiences, our thoughts, judgements and beliefs as well as our cultural experiences. It is a webbed energy mind pattern connecting us with God; universal mind consciousness; the mind of other people; the mind of nature, i.e., stone people, trees, animals, insects, etc., and the elementals earth, air, water, and fire. The universal mind consciousness is the collective consciousness. It is the energy pattern of all the thoughts ever thought, i.e., myths, archetypes, etc. It is the consciousness of the current thoughts of the human race. The mental body provides us with ideas, clarity, and concepts necessary for our physical lives. It links us to infinite storage and processes of information and is the engine for alignment and ascension into Divine and Christ consciousness.

In this book the fourth through the eighth auric field are referred to as the spiritual body. The fourth auric field surrounds the body and is uniquely shaped according to our relationships with others, our ancestors and God. It is integrative, communicative and self regulating with the fourth Chakra located in the center of the chest, the Heart energy center. Through the front side of the heart chakra, this energy field integrates us with those with whom we have formed relationships in this lifetime (Dale,149). The energy stream of Divine Love flows through this auric field , to the back side of the heart chakra. The fourth auric field also holds the relational energy which connects us to our ancestors. This auric field enables us to have out- of- body experiences and transcends time and distance, as we know it, in our waking state. We can visit ancestors, friends on the other side of the continent, or experience future events. It is the relationship field but is also known as the dreaming body. It can go through a wall, fly, and do other things that the physical body cannot do. When I was on my third vision quest, I was taken wrapped up in my vision blanket back in time to review my life. I remember walking through walls and flying from place to place. I was then taken forward to see the effect of changes that I was being guided to make. This auric field can be used in times of need when we want help beyond our three dimensional experience.

The fifth auric field is referred to by Cyndi Dale in *New Chakra Healing* as the parallel field. She describes this field as an opening to other parallel dimensions. A parallel dimension is another space or plane of existence that exists simultaneously with the one we know and experience.   Parallel dimensions are often the subject of science fiction. It was a major componet of the plot in the movie "Back to the Future". The TV show "Deep Space Nine" featured an on going series of episodes where Avery Brooks, Captain Benjamin Cisco, was transported to a parallel dimension. The same people existed in this other dimension, but their lives and relationship to Cisco were different. My experiences with parallel dimensions generally occur when I am outside. I will see the place where I am as it was one hundred or two hundred years ago. I am simultaneously looking at the current scene and at the same time seeing the scene two hundred years ago. The receiver for experiencing other dimensions is the fifth auric field. According to Dale, images, forms, ideas, and messages from other dimensions are reversed in their reception by the back side aspect of the fifth auric field (Dale,150). The mirror image then hits the lens- like aspect of the front side of the fifth auric field where it is reversed, so that we can understand it and integrate it into our Body.. This reversal of image and correction of image is exactly the way we see in this dimension.

In several episodes of Deep Space Nine, Captain Cisco was summoned (or kidnaped) into the parallel dimension. Generally, this summoning occurred when there was a crisis in that dimension, and he was needed to take an action that his parallel counterpart self was unable to take. Likewise for us, this dimension can be accessed when we need another perspective, an alternate view of ourselves, to find a different way of responding to a current situation or the need to see a whole other realm of possibilities. The fifth auric field crosses in a figure eight at the fifth Chakra, located at the hollow of the throat. The fifth auric layer is integrative, communicative and self regulating with the fifth Chakra. The fifth Chakra assists with the process of finding a different way since it is the Chakra that provides us with guidance from our soul self.

The sixth auric field is the Light Body which is seen as a glow of light around the body. I remember being told stories of how the elders could light the way for the people or illuminate an enclosure for ceremony with the light of their bodies. It is the link to the white Light of

God, the Divine Source. This auric field enables us to be the light of the world. Its connection to the sixth Chakra, the third eye located between the eyebrows, enables us to see beyond the physical illusion to the meta physical. One illustration of seeing beyond the illusion is in the movie, The Matrix, when Neo, the main character, sees the actual computer binary codes that form the image of the aliens who police the computer generated illusion world of humans. In seeing those codes, Neo transcends the illusion. We transcend the physical illusion when we experience the divine within. The sixth auric field is integrated, communicative and self regulated with the sixth Chakra and enables us to end separation from our divine consciousness.

The seventh auric field has an egg shaped appearance. This field affects our entire existence. I refer to it as the connecting field. It connects us to God. It connects with all the other aura fields. It also links the seventh Chakra located at the top of the head, to the tenth or grounding Chakra beneath the feet. Thus, the seventh auric field connects heaven, which is our illuminated state of divine consciousness, with earth, which is our material and physical body consciousness.

The eighth auric field connects all our memories with present time. I refer to it as the memory field. It can assist us to remember our purpose for incarnating in this life time, and enables us to access all we have ever done, been or said. It is connected at the crown of our head spreading energy around our Body and is attached to the Chakras. It is integrative, communicative and self regulative with the eighth Chakra located above the head. These fields have different vibratory rates. The first, second and third fields vibrate at a slower rate than the fourth through eighth fields . The fields with the highest vibratory rate are the sixth, seventh and eighth.

The etheric field is a bridge between the physical body and the other aspects of our Body and contains matter with three different vibratory rates molecules, atoms and sub-atomic particles. Molecules are atoms held together by electromagnetic energy vibrating at a slower rate. Atoms are held together internally by electromagnetic energy, and their vibratory rate is faster than molecules. Atoms are patterns of subatomic particles. Subatomic particles are pure energy. Energy that is everywhere and incessantly assuming first this form and then that form. It is at the subatomic level that mass is converted to energy and energy to mass. Thus it is through the etheric bridge that emotions and thoughts are able to create physically manifested disease.   The second, third, and fourth fields are pure energy or subatomic particles. The second auric field, the emotional body, is energy-in-motion. It's vibratory rate changes with each emotion, therefore it is incessantly vibrating at the rate of first this emotion then that emotion. The type of emotions, type of thoughts, and type of relationships can raise or lower the vibration rate of the second, third and fourth auric fields and that energy vibrating through the etheric field bridge either maintains health or creates physically manifested disease.

The sixth, seventh and eight fields are subatomic and light energy. These last three auric fields connect us to the Light of God, which comes to us as light energy consisting of protons that are wave-like in their movement. Light energy, because of its wave-like movement, is subject to interference. For example, if we dropped two stones (A and B) in a pond simultaneously and watched the waves spreading towards each other from the point of entry of the stones, the waves that each stone makes would interfere with one another. In

21

instances where the crest of the wave of one stone A meets the crest of the wave of stone B, large waves would result. As in the ocean, the crests of multiple small waves come together to creae a large wave. But in instances where the crest of the wave of stone A meets the trough of the wave of stone B, the water is calm. This occurs because the trough of stone B as a wave 'depression' is able to absorb the volume of water of the crest of the wave of stone A. The trough of the wave of stone B can be likened to interference. The 'depression' that characterizes the trough of stone B is analogous to a lowered vibratory rate and the crest of stone A, is analogous to a higher vibratory rate. The result is that the lower fibratory rate i.e. trough of stone B interfers with the higher vibratory rate i.e., crest of stone A. Thus, the crest is no longer a crest it has been interfered with by the trough, lowered and the water is calm. Simularly the light energy of God, illuminated consciousness, are like crests these light energy waves have a high vibratory rate. Negative self talk and judgements are like troughs this type of material consciousness has a low vibratory rate. It is interference. When interference occurs the sixth, seventh and eighth fields vibratory rate is lowered. Thus, interference of material consciousness lowers the vibratory rate of our sixth, seventh and eighth energy fields. This is when we are in upset, are sick, feel stuck or are in struggle. Illuminated Consciousness overcomes interference. The protons of the light energy waves respond to our consciousness because they are conscious. When illuminated consciousness meets illuminated consciousness, it is like the crest of two waves coming together increasing the vibratory rate of the fields. Our consciousness directing the light energy increases illumination, love, healing, balance, being on purpose, and manifesting our desires easily and effortlessly.

Chapter One Summary

1. When we recognate an experience and surrender to the process, the pain of change diminishes.

2. Our Body vibrates at different vibratory speeds giving the physical, emotional, mental, and spiritual aspect of our Body different appearances but it is one Body.

3. The auric system is an energy field consisting of eight basic fields moving in a figure eight pattern these fields have different vibratory rates.

4. The point where the figure eight intersects is an energy vortex the properties of which integrate the Auric system with the Chakras and the physical body,

5. The eight auric fields are: first the etheric, second emotional, third mental, fourth relational, fifth parallel, sixth light, seventh connecting, and eighth memory.

East

The East is illumination. As the sun rises,
so our consciousness is raised by the
eastern energy. The rising Sun of
consciousness brings light to shadow.

Chapter Two
Our Inner Life

When a man begins to develop his senses,
so that he may see a little more than everyone sees,
a new and most fascinating world opens before him,
and the chakras are among the first objects in that
world to attract his attention. His fellow-men present
themselves under a fresh aspect; he perceives much
with regard to them which was previously hidden from
his eyes, and he is therefore able to understand, to
appreciate and (when necessary) to help them much
better than he could before.
C.W. Leadbeater, The Chakras

The Pattern Buffers

Because we are open energy systems in continuous interchange with the energy ocean, something has to keep our energy pattern in an organized form. On Star Trek, when the crew needs to beam down, there is a pattern buffer in the transporter that holds the pattern of each crew member until they rematerialize. Chakras are our pattern buffers. They are the energy vortex melding our energies and holding them together in pattern as a definite unique living organism. The seven 'in- body' chakras hold the pattern of the physical body, the molecules, cells, etc, and the auric fields that are integrated with those charkas. The two upper 'out- of- body' chakras hold the celestial connection pattern of our divine purpose and unique manifestation of God. The two lower 'out- of-body' chakras hold the materials form for manifesting. The upper and lower 'out- of -body' Chakras hold the pattern for the auric fields integrated with those Chakras.The seventh auric field integrates with the tenth

25

Chakra and the eight auric field integrates with the eighth Chakra. The front side of the Chakras relate to the present moment. The back side to past moments. The Chakras combined purpose is to regulate the Body in a dynamic oneness assisting growth, development, health and healing. Their function is to integrate the Body (physical, auric) and maintain a continuous dynamic link with energy from the Source. Our state of consciousness determines the level and direction of growth, development, health and healing. Chakras receive and transmit God's Light and Love, integrating us with the One giving us a shared existence relative to all beings, assisting us to bring forth our unique manifestation of the One and our purpose relative to the scheme of things. Our state of consciousness determines the degree to which we receive God's Light and Love, the degree to which we are integrated and realize our purpose.

The more we understand about Chakras, the more we are able to appreciate that we are grounded God-energy. We are like the rays of the sun upon the earth. Grounded sunlight is not separated from its source. And neither are we. Chakras are the key to ourselves as an open energy system, a unified whole that is dynamic yet in balance. An open system is in constant interchange with its Source.

The word Chakra is a Sanskrit word meaning wheel or revolving disc this word discribes the seven in-body Chakra. But Chakras are not flat discs; they are conical streams of energy vibrating at a particular frequency or rate. Our state of consciousness determines the vibratory rate. With the seven in-body chakras, the narrow stem part of the cone's stream of energy is anchored at specific points on the spine in the dense physical body, passing through that dense body on the front side and back sides;

with the wider part of the cone linking it with the emotional, mental, and spiritual bodies/auric field at the point where the auric fields figure eight energy crosses. (See figure 2)

Like a wheel, in-body Chakras have spokes, but each Chakra has a different number of spokes and spins at a different rate. The rate of spin results in a different vibratory frequency for each Chakra. Think of a guitar. Each string has a different thickness, tautness and when struck vibrates at a different rate producing a different tone. It is important to remember that each Chakra has a different number of spokes and spins at a different rate because, in healing the Chakras, each responds to a different musical tone.

A healthy in-body Chakra rotates oscillating at a particular rate and receives energy flow of Prana or Divine Source energy or Chi flowing from the Source. The in-body Chakras receive energy of a particular characteristic wave length that induces secondary forces, which spin around the Chakra, passing over and under each other in undulations. Each undulation is a multiple of the wave length within it. There are thousands of wave lengths in one undulation. The difference in the number of spokes of each Chakra is created by these oscillating undulations of different sizes crossing each other in basket-work fashion (Leadbeater, 8). According to Leadbeater, the crossing of the oscillating undulations of different sizes produces the petal like spokes of the in-body Chakra. Though each is operating at its own optimal vibratory frequency, the frequencies are interrelated. If one Chakra is not synchronous, the others are thrown off balance also. Generally, it is the Chakra above and below the non synchronous one that is effected. This is why in doing Chakra healing work we pay attention to all the Chakras.

figure 2

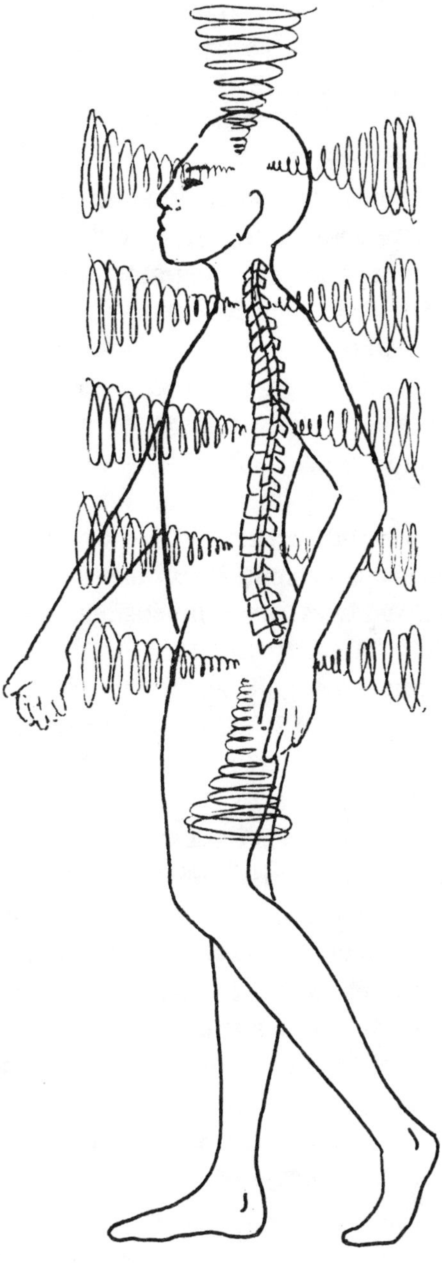

The Seven In-Body Chakras Front and Back Side

The in-body chakras act like a prism, breaking up energy into component colors, dispatching the color to the Chakra or part of the body for which it is needed. Colors are particles moving at different speeds so that each in-body Chakra has a vibratory synchrony with a particular color. Colors are also important in healing each Chakra.

The front and back side of the in-body Chakra attaches to the spine. The mouth extends just pass the skin to the juncture where the auric field figure eight crosses that energy vortex is integrative, communicative and self regulative with the corresponding auric field. In the front, the Chakra spins clock/sunwise. In the back, it spins counter clock/moon wise. A counter clockwise spin facilitates releasing. "The front side of the chakric system relates to our conscious self, our day-to-day reality. Thus containing information and imprints from this life. The back side pertains to that which is behind us or that which is unconscious. It includes information and imprints from past lives, other dimensions, and other worlds" (Dale,113).

As an energy stream, the anchoring of the in-body Chakras to the spine is a vibrational anchoring, which occurs when two energy streams pulsate at the same frequency coming together as if holding hands or fitting together like the pieces of a jigsaw puzzle. This vibrational anchoring is possible because the spine and the other bones of the body are crystalline formations of atoms joined together in perfect unity and harmony giving them the physical properties that we know as bone. As with other crystalline structures, the spinal bones have the ability to amplify, transform, store, focus, and transfer energy. To amplify means to increase the strength of. When the Source's energy reaches the spinal bones, it is increased. Transform means to change in form, appearance or condition. For example, quartz, when cut into precise shapes, vibrates at precise rates and transforms electricity into waves which can be broadcast, as in radio and television signals. I intuit that the shape of the spinal column is precisely designed to transform Source energy into specialized light energy waves. The variation in size of the spinal column, i.e., larger vertebra at the lower body and smaller at the upper body, has to do with the vibratory frequencies that vertebra are designed to receive and transmit. The in-body Chakras, from the abdomen down, vibrate at a lower frequency than does the in-body Chakras from the heart to the crown. The specialized energy light waves can be stored, focused, and/or transferred back to the Chakras. Thus, the in-body Chakras utilize these abilities of the spinal column to amplify, transform, store, focus and transfer energy in linking the four bodies (physical, mental, emotional and spiritual).

The out-of-body Chakras can be visualized as cylindical spirals of energy connecting with the physical body and moving energy from the invisible to visible, from the spiritual to the material. These spirals are composed of two types of energy, one that moves slower than the speed of light or quanta and one that moves faster than the speed of light or tachyon (Dale,24). An example of quanta energies are the elemental energies from which the earth or material plane is created: earth, air, fire, and water. These same elementals alone or in various combinations can be utilized in the healing of the seven in-body chakras. An example of the faster-than-the-speed-of- light energies are celestial energies and sexual energy. These also have a healing function. The out-of body Chakras consist of quanta elemental energies, tachyon celestial energy and sexual energy enabling them to link the spiritual with the material. The out-of-body

Chakras do not have spokes. The two upper out-of-body Chakras contain and are communicative with celestial energies and sexual energies. The two lower out-of-body Charkas. contain and are communicative with elemental energies. Thus, as a system they integrate and are self regulating in regards to elemental and celestial energies.

The communication system is used by all the Chakras to integrate the four bodies, the future, ancestors, past lives, and maintain our connection to the Creator. The communication system consists of physical, psychic, and intuitive communication. Physical communication solicits, processes, and sends energy through the physical body. Examples of physical communication are the use of language, physical sensations, crying, dumping waste from the physical and emotional bodies, and receiving elemental and magnetic energy from the ground and feeding it to the physical energy system. Psychic communication, which is faster than the speed of light, receives, processes and sends energy to the emotional and mental bodies. Examples of psychic communication are physical empathy, which is the registration of physical sensations that belong to someone else; feeling empathy, which is the ability to experience another person's feelings; receiving and sending healing energy; and clair audience, which is the ability to hear or speak psychically to guides or other people. Intuitive communication receives, processes, and sends energy to the spiritual body. Examples of intuitive communication are channeling guides, insight, inspiration (in-spirit-a-tion, the incoming consciousness of spirit), and knowledge of life purposes.

Our eleven Chakras, as a communication system, receive and transmitt the various planes of existence or dimensions. In this sense, the Chakras are analogous to radio receivers. The God Station, or WGOD/GS communicates and sends messages from God, Angels, your Divine Self, Ascended Masters, etc. Who you hear depends upon the vibratory level of your radio receiver/Chakra which is infleuenced by your state of consciousness. Angels, your Divine Self, Ascended Masters, or other people are "stepped down" aspects of God/Divine intelligence. Stepped down aspects of WGOD vibrate at the level of our consciousness. So we have WGOD/angels, WGOD/ancestors, WGOD/ascended masters, WGOD/guides, WGOD/ people, WGOD/Divine Self. One Source but different stations for different states of consciousness, playing what you need to hear for your spiritual evolution. WGOD/stations constantly flood Chakras with Light energy impulses at the vibrational levels congruent with the vibrational frequency your Chakra can receive. Sometimes there is interference in the form of judgements, which block the reception of messages and Light energy. We are in a trough, just as we sometimes get interference on our radio blocking the reception.

The Body Map: Our Chakas

The Chakras are the map to our Body. If you have the map, you can read what is going on and make the correction in your course. If you do not have the map, you're lost, stuck in the same repeating patterns, missing your goals, feeling powerless, and assigning all sorts of meanings to what is occurring in your Body, most of which are inaccurate. This next section describes each of the eleven Chakra that you will work with in the fourth chapter. (See figure 3) The Judgements, Thoughts, Emotions, Behavior, and Physical descriptions and the Chakra stories discussed in this section give the functions

Figure 3

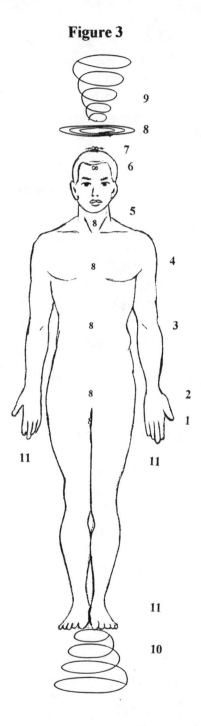

The Eleven Chakras

of the Chakras and examples of Chakras oscillating at a lower vibrational rate because of energy blocks. The Location, Spokes, Age of Development, Color, Spiritual Goal apply to all chakras. The Element, Color, Musical Note, Breath Cycle, and God Conscious Decision are tools for increasing the vibratory rate of the Chakra to optimal.

Become familiar with the information about each Chakra. As you read, note instances where the descriptions match your patterns. At the end of the discussion of each Chakra, there is a Chakra story. This story summarizes and illustrates the information covered in the description as it shows up in life. Each story is an illustrative composite of issues related to the Chakra discussed as they were presented by various clients with whom I've worked. Composites of the issues and changing the name has been done to protect clients' identities. When I work with a client I assist them to identify the issue. In the course of a counseling session we identify the judgement and the related Chakra. Generally there are more than one affected Chakra. During the session we release, using Quantum Dynamic's Transformation breath, the judgement, the thought, and the emotion that block energy as they exist currently as well as all past copies. Clients are then coached though creating and completing action steps that change the behaviors. Their cycle of miscreation is identified and multiple interventions designed to break the cycle. This process can occur in one session or over multiple sessions. I rarely work with clients for longer than three months.

First Chakra
Location
The first Chakra is called the base or root Chakra. The front side of it is anchored in the body at the fourth sacral vertebrae and surfaces at the base of the spine or the tail bone/coccyx. The back side is located in a lower dimension based in the universal pool of physical matter from which all life begins.

Spokes
The Earth's love energy, and fire energy undulates in such a manner as to give the appearance of four spokes/a cross.

Age of Development
Womb to 6 months

Judgement That Blocks Energy
I'm Wrong, I'm right, They're wrong - decisions about our fundamental right to exist, our right to be loved, and to have our needs met; programming affecting our basic survival needs, such as food, shelter, water, sexuality; our roots, ancestral and family values as well as all our prior experiences in other lifetimes.

Thought That Blocks Energy
Obstruction- a mental state that blocks how successful we are at surviving, blocks our abundance, and how able we are to receive material assistance and keep our incoming will to live alive.

Emotions That Blocks Energy
Anger- This is the predominant conscious emotion that blocks love energy from entering the backside of this chakra. Anger is a response to not having experiences occur the way we judge that they should occur. The unconscious emotion experienced is fear. Fear about survival is a major preoccupation.

Behavior When Energy is Blocked

Behaviors include *perfectionism,* i.e., wanting things to be exactly as you envision them. The ideal is visioned in the head, and everything is compared to it; *getting stuck* arises when we cannot manifest the ideal envisioned; *avoidance* of taking action and *delays* in taking action especially because we've judged ourselves as unable to accomplish the ideal. There is *regret* and *isolation* from other people. First chakra issues also show up behaviorally as depression and suicidal thoughts or actions.

Physical Manifestations of Blocked Energy

Circulatory problems - the blood is our love energy circulating throughout our body; poor circulation affects our hands and feet, which are needed for survival; our feet ground us; *rectal problems-* reflect dealing with our world, letting go; *urinary tract problems-* anger and failure to express anger *chemical imbalances* depression and psychiatric problems; *dental problems-* insecure foundations, inability to breakdown reality and deal with it, irritation with mother . *Anger* turns into physical problems that boil, burn, and infect our body.

Healing Element

Prana, vitality, God's Light and Love

Healing Musical Note

The key of A, music using deep low drums, or the bassoon. Sound LAM (begins with an open mouth with L, comes to the center of the mouth with A as in India, and ends with lips closed in M)

Color

Chakra color is orange, deep red to bright red; healing color is white and pink

Healing Breath cycle
1/4 second: 1/8 second on the inhale and 1/8 second on
the exhale. This is the bellows breath, a short inhale with
the emphasis on the exhale using the abdominal muscles
contraction to force the exhale.

Spiritual Goal
Surrender to Divine Law; realization that we are a unique
physical manifestation of God; willingness to allow
unlimited amounts of Divine energy to flow through this
Chakra and shape our physical experiences; trust and
development of an abundance consciousness.

God Conscious Decision
I surrender; I'm happy in my unlimited abundance.

First Chakra Story
Sylvia is a perfectionist. She has very high standards for
herself. In fact sometimes these standards get in the way
of her accomplishing things. Sometimes she gets stuck
completing projects because she can't get it perfect or up
to her standards. Sylvia is angry about a lot of things that
she feels is wrong with the world. She has a strong value
system and is quick to judge situations and people as
wrong. Once she has judged someone as wrong, she feels
justified in whatever actions she takes. Sylvia attempts to
be right in everything she does and has a lot of difficulty
accepting that she may have misjudged a situation. It
makes her angry if someone says she is wrong or attempts
to show her a different way to do something. Right and
wrong are a vicious cycle. She has to be right because the
consequences of being wrong trigger survival fear. In her
right and wrong judgements, she doesn't trust other
people because they don't know how to do things right.
Her favorite quote is, "If you want it done right, do it
yourself." She neglects herself in terms of fixing up her

apartment, buying herself clothes, and caring for her health needs. Even though she earns a decent salary she never feels she has enough money. She always feels deprived or deficient in some way.

Second Chakra

Location

The front side is located in the genital area. The back side in the sacral lower back area.

Spokes

Utilizes energy coming from the sun, which is poured out or undulates in such a manner as to give the appearance of six petals or divisions.

Age of Development

6 months to 2 ½ years

Judgement That Blocks Energy.

Aliveness Hurts or Kills- is a decision about the awareness of feelings, trusting feelings and expression of feelings, creativity, sexuality, reproduction and gestation of babies, ideas, projects etc., In fact, the very expression of the Life energy is blocked, which includes healing, playfulness, joy, and pleasure.

Thought That Blocks Energy

Hostile -a mental state that interferes with the full expression and experiencing of our own and other peoples' feelings, and our own creativity. A tendency to battle life, thus blocking the Life energy needed to feel, and blocking receiving the adaptation energy needed to cope with life's changes.

Emotions That Block Energy

Hostility -This is the predominant conscious emotion. Other emotions include experiencing one- self as being insufficient, apathetic, and attempting to appease. Appeasement manifests as abuse issues. Experiences of judging oneself as accountable for everything shows up as co- dependency issues. The ability to balance and adapt to the duality of physical existence, i.e., good and bad, truth and falsehood, in a flexible creative way is diminished. Also diminished is the ability to keep feelings in balance and not over react to life's changes, and to be fully present in the world.

Behavior When Energy is Blocked
Extreme reactions bordering on wanting to kill, murderous actions, criticism, gossip, and pushy aggressiveness.

Physical Manifestations When Energy is Blocked
Infections of all types, including boils, stress, lower back pain, allergies, migraines, and accident proneness (that is related to not being fully present in the world); disease in the reproductive (genital organs) system as well as sexual dysfunction, sexual manipulation, sterility, and sexual abuse. Criticism indulged in long enough will manifest physically as arthritis.

Healing Element
Fire, actual fire or the symbol of fire

Healing Note
The note of C. Instruments such as rhythm instruments, saxophone, marimbas, electric bass guitar. Sound VAM (V at the back of a open mouth, A as in father, and M with the lips closed)

Healing Breath Cycle
½ second: an inhale and an exhale within the span of ½ second. It is similar to a panting breath or the bellows breath used in Hatha yoga.

Color
Chakra color includes various shades of red with some green in it. Healing color: pastel peach, violet.

Spiritual Goal
Recognizing that aliveness heals; trusting the expression of feelings; drawing life from both the earthy and the

spiritual side so that there is balance; experiencing pleasure in the body; allowing divine consciousness to unfold and bringing that consciousness into expression in the body.

God Conscious Decision

My aliveness heals; My pleasure pleases God

Second Chakra Story

Pauline is a gossip. She is very critical of everyone, and when she is feeling especially hostile toward someone she will say, "Oh I could just kill him." She has allergies, repeated infections, and is accident prone. People perceive her as cold because she doesn't express her feelings. She has difficulty coping with change and, therefore, tends to be controlling. In her church she's the one that everyone comes to for help because she's willing to help people manage their lives. She is married but has no children having had several miscarriages.

Third Chakra

Location

The third Chakra front side is located in the navel area. Intuitively, I've been guided to locate the third Chakra in feminine energy as below the navel. I refer to this area as the lunar plexus, (a plexus is a network of nerves). The third Chakra in masculine energy is above the navel, referred to as the solar plexus. The backside is in the middle of the back in proximity to the eighth thoracic vertebrae.

Spokes

Vibrates solar energy (masculine creative energy) and lunar energy (feminine creative energy) in such a manner as to give the appearance of ten divisions or undulations.

Age of Development

2 ½ to 4 ½ years

Judgement That Blocks Energy

Unworthy to receive - This judgement blocks personal power, our achievement in the world, and our will to achieve (however each of us defines achievement). The front side expresses our will in the world while the back side enables the drive for achievement. This Chakra is also the mind of the body. The mind is the essence or vibration of mental and emotional function, the channel through which we receive the divine impulses of God, which are ideas, thoughts or understandings. The area where this chakra is anchored also contains tissue similar to brain tissue. The organic substance of brain tissue controls mental, physical and emotional functions. To say the third chakra is the mind of the body means that this center enables ideas, thoughts, or intellectual understandings to register at a gut or mental-physical-emotional level simultaneously. When this occurs, it is intuitive cognition, the direct perception of truth experienced as an inner knowing or an immediate keen insight that cannot be explained by reasoning. Thus, the third chakra is the seat of our intuitive cognition. It is the mind/body connection. In masculine energy, that intuitive understanding or inner knowingness is felt in the solar plexus, and in feminine energy, it is felt in the lunar plexus. When there is a blocked energy, we doubt or question that intuitive cognition. We do not act upon it and block the manifestation of this knowing. As a result, our self-esteem and self-confidence are affected because we do not trust our inner knowing.

Thought That Blocks Energy

Loss - a mental state of deprivation or separation that can bring about a failure to preserve or maintain mental and intellectual energy for success, to interface with the world, deal with the world, and make effective decisions. The back side serves as the intellectual template through which judgements are processed, accepted, changed, or rejected.

Emotions That Block Energy

Hate- this is the predominant conscious emotion. Other emotions include feeling undeserving as well as despair or hopeless. It is the storehouse for opinions and beliefs we have gathered about ourselves in this lifetime (front side) and in past life times (back side). This chakra enables us to totally accept ourselves, our purposes, and our drives. When hate is the predominant conscious emotion, it is ourselves, our purposes, and our drives that are hated. We experience ourselves as undeserving, and the punishing of ourselves gives rise to despair/hopelessness. We lack faith and don't trust our divine inspiration.

Behavior When Energy is Blocked

Scarcity is the predominant behavior: Experiencing the self as lacking such things as love, money, sexual fulfillment, power in relation to ourselves, others and the world. Imbalance is expressed in the use of power and love. There is an imbalance in the use of power and love resulting in co-dependency and caretaking issues, both of which mix love and power. Difficulty receiving from others. Other behaviors include hiding our gifts, skills, talents as well as continually creating the experience of loss in our lives that can be relational, economic, or physical including amputation of limbs or surgical removal of organs.

Physical Manifestation of Blocked Energy

The energy of the third chakra affects the abdominal organs with each organ reflecting a different issue. For example, liver problems indicate masculine energy issues around anger; it also harbors our fear of life; spleen reflects feminine energy issues around anger and balancing the use of anger for our personal protection; stomach indicates digesting opinions and judgements from others, digesting our reality and emotional nourishment; gallbladder indicates grief about men (this applies to men and women) or our use of masculine energy, including our achievement in the world; gallbladder also represents bitterness; pancreas indicates issues around receiving the sweetness of life including expressing and integrating love; the adrenal glands represent our belief about our creative responses to danger or opportunities; and the kidneys hold our childhood perceptions regarding emotional needs and represents holding onto old emotional patterns.

Unresolved third chakra issues can develop into the creation of organ loss and loss of limbs. The loss of a limb dramatically impacts our ability to take action in the world.

Healing Element
Actual water and air or the symbols of water and air.

Healing Musical Note
The note of A sharp (A#). Musical compositions with the guitar, viola, cello, piano, organ, and/or clarinet. Sound RAM (follow previous descriptions for making the sounds).

Healing Breath Cycle
One second: ½ second on the inhale and ½ second on the exhale.

Color
The Chakra color is a mixture of light red with green and orange. Healing colors are yellow to gold as well as violet and ruby.

Spiritual Goal
Having faith in our ability to carry out our divine purpose, including the ideas necessary to envision and implement our goals. The ability to know the seen and the unseen. Trusting in-spirit-a-tion. To experience total support in moving forth in the world, utilizing the masculine and feminine energy in a balanced way to bring forth ideas into the world. Service to humanity.

God Conscious Decision
I joyfully express my God-given ideas; God loves through me.

Third Chakra Story
Oliver never thought he deserved anything. No matter how hard he worked, he could never accumulate any wealth. He had nothing to show for his labor. He felt that he could not hold onto friends. Every time he made a friend, he would lose that friendship. His marriage had ended in divorce. In his relationships with people, he always found himself embroiled in a power struggle, which he always lost. He hated his life and hated people who had "made it." He didn't trust himself and was always second guessing his decisions. This resulted in him not getting work in on time and his inability to present his ideas to management in an authoritative way. Thus, he was always passed over for promotions. His doctor recently told him that he was developing diabetes, which sent him into panic because his father died from complications of diabetes.

Fourth Chakra
Location
Referred to as the heart Chakra, the front side it is located to the right of the heart over the breast bone near the pulmonary plexus and the cardiac plexus. The back side is at the end of the thoracic spinal area and the beginning of the cervical spinal area or upper back area just where the shoulder blades begin.

Spokes
Divine unconditional love energy undulates in such a manner as to give the appearance of twelves spokes.

Age of Development
4 ½ to 6 ½ years

Judgement That Blocks Energy

I'm not enough, I'm too much - decisions about love, the meaning of love in our life relationships with self and others. Mercy, compassion, forgiveness, and acceptance of self and others. Free expression of self and our desires as well as the use of emotions in our transformation. The judgement, *I'm not Enough, I'm too Much*, creates an emotional roller coaster, taking us from the heights of loving and feeling loved and being productive to the depths of not loving the self, emotional bankruptcy, unexpressed desires, and total failure.

Thought That Blocks Energy

Sterility- a mental state that renders us barren or unproductive. Specifically, we are incapable of manifesting the offspring of our consciousness--our ideas. It is emotion (the feminine principle) that combines with consciousness (the masculine principle) to manifest the idea or quality desired.

Emotion That Blocks Energy

Resentment - This is the predominant conscious emotion that blocks the presence of unconditional love. Resentment is the opposite of gratitude. Resentment supports the belief in lack and failure. This choice leads to self abasement or degrading the self, destruction of self confidence, and the terror that accompanies that choice. .

Behavior When Energy is Blocked

This center balances the divine energy of the upper Chakras with the material life force energies of the lower Chakras. When it is blocked, the resulting behaviors are nonproductivity alternating with prolific activity, and temperamental and uneven emotional responses.

Physical Manifestation of Blocked Energy

The heart is the balance between heaven and earth. Heaven is the realization of divine ideas, and earth is the manifestation of those ideas. Heart problems are indications of an imbalance between the realization of divine ideas and the manifestation of those ideas. Specifically there is too much focusing on the material and not expressing heavenly consciousness; and not expressing love. Lung problems reflect feelings about ourselves and the ability to inhale life. Coughing, indicates that we are choking on life. A stiff neck prevents turning of the head and represents a narrow viewpoint. Resentment held for a long time festers and becomes tumors or cancer of the lung or throat. In combination with other blocked Chakras, cancer can manifest in other places. For example, the fourth Chakra with the second Chakra creates prostate or uterine cancer.

Healing Element
Air and fire, actual air and fire or the symbols of air and fire.

Healing Musical Note
The key of D and music using the instruments of the harp, violin, piano, cello, flute, zither. The healing sound isYAM.

Color
The Chakra color is a glowing golden color. The healing color is pink.

Healing Breath Cycle
2 seconds: one second on the inhale and one second on the exhale.

Spiritual Goal
Acceptance of and living the presence of God's unconditional Divine Love. Acknowledging and living our spirit's true desire. Self Love

God Conscious Decision
I Am Love in Balance; The Universe is Perfect.

Fourth Chakra Story
Mae's life was like a roller coaster. Sometimes she was very prolific in her work as a designer with lots of new ideas and projects. When she was like this, none of her staff could keep up with her. At other times she was

unproductive. In those times, she felt like a failure. She would look at the work of other designers and become resentful of what they had produced. She would look at what she had done and criticize it as awful. When her staff would disagree with her, she would become indignant, telling them that they were insulting her intelligence. In those moments, she felt unloved and unsupported. She experienced resentment of her life and the people with whom she had relationships. Her staff viewed her as temperamental, attributed to her creative genius. Mae was terrified about these slumps of nonproductive. In these slumps, there were times when she was overwhelmed by anxiety, and her heart raced. She would think about all the things she had not accomplished. Other times she was exhausted, and her heart would feel like it was hardly beating. She kept going to the doctor but was told there was nothing physically wrong with her heart. It was difficult for her to stay in a relationship with anyone. She would start out being very passionate, then would question whether or not she deserved better or was good enough for this person. Eventually, the relationship would just fizzle out as she withdrew her emotional investment in it.

Fifth Chakra

Location

The front side is located at the hollow of the throat. The back side is located at the back of the neck at the third cervical vertebrae.

Spokes

The energy of this Chakra undulates in such a manner as to give the appearance of sixteen spokes.

Age of Development

6 ½ to 8 ½ years

Judgement That Blocks Energy

I'm Unlovable, Unworthy of God's Love - decisions about worthiness that impact our ability to manifest what we want in life by speaking our desires, saying what we want or don't want to experience and speaking our truth. Difficulty communicating verbally, sharing emotions, and information. The back side enables us to be open to guidance from others as well as from our spiritual or God Self. The judgement, *I'm Unlovable, Unworthy of God's Love*, blocks us from receiving that guidance, especially from our God Self. Blocks our ability to hear or speak psychically to our higher self and, therefore, to create the circumstances necessary to achieve our purpose.

Thought That Blocks Energy

Rejection - a mental state that refuses to accept, admit or recognize self-worth, the expression of desires, the right to manifest and communicate needs, desires or beliefs, wisdom, and responsibility.

Emotions That Block Energy

Pain - This is the predominant conscious emotion. The avoidance of emotional pain results in inability to say "yes" or "no." The avoidance of responsibility or taking on too much responsibility is another manifestation of the inability to say "yes"or "no." Other emotions present are guilt, especially after being assertive; guilt always seeks punishment in the form of pain; blame assists in the avoidance of responsibility. There is grief over the loss of self-worth, and anxiety is generally about experiencing emotional pain.

Behavior When Energy is Blocked

Victimization, creating experiences of being misunderstood or not being heard, experiencing the self as unlovable, being rejected by others and experiencing profound emotional pain at each experience of rejection by others. Giving the Body over to other entities i.e., allowing outside energies both human and other dimensional to enter our Body without exercising discretion. Giving the body over to outside entities without discretion is the ultimate expression of abdication of responsibility. For in doing so, we surrender our self-consciousness.

Physical Manifestation of Blocked Energy

The neck is the bridge between two states of mind, the ideal (heaven) and the manifestation of the ideal (earth). It is the bridge between the mind and the body. Food we take in through the head passes to the body to nourish or malnourish the body. Similarly, thoughts from the head manifest in the body. The throat and the use of sound is a vehicle for manifestation. Our speech is the lowest vibration of the spiral of sound which created the various planes of existence. The power of the spoken word is the power to ascend that spiral with consciousness using the inner quality and power of sound.

Physical problems in this area are indicative of blockage in the function of the throat. Infection in the throat implies irritation and holding back of energy by not saying what we really want or conflict in expressing ourselves;cancer here reflects not voicing resentment; inflammation and soreness reflects trying to close down or cut off our physical reality. An underactive thyroid indicates giving up, especially grief; an overactive thyroid indicates rage at not being loved or not being heard.

Healing Element

Water and fire, actual fire and water or the symbols of fire and water.

Healing Musical Note

The key of G sharp (G#), and music using the instruments of the human voice, flute, or woodwinds. Sound HAM

Color

The Chakra color is blue with some green. Healing color is cobalt blue.

Healing Breath Cycle

4 seconds: 2 seconds on the inhale and 2 seconds on the exhale.

Spiritual Goal

Speak the truth and wisdom of our Divine self. Full incorporation of our soul's purpose. Ability to hear Divine instructions (clair audience).

God Conscious Decision

I'm Creative; God Accepts Me.

Fifth Chakra Story

Howard was bashful, soft-spoken, and felt that no one understood him. He had anxiety attacks that seemed to come from nowhere, at least he could never pinpoint what triggered his anxiety. He tried very hard at work to do what others expected of him. If he did what others told him to do and something went wrong, he could blame them. Even though he was very accommodating to everyone, he still believed that his co-workers rejected him, and that hurt. Going to work, staying at work, and experiencing his co-worker's rejection was emotionally painful. But he knew that if he didn't work, his marriage was over.

He was married to a very aggressive woman who was verbally abusive. He stayed in the relationship because she took care of everything. All he had to do was go to work, come home, and give her his pay check. She picked out his clothes, cooked his meals, and they socialized with her friends. All he had to do was show up.

Sixth Chakra

Location

Referred to as the brow Chakra, the front side is located in the space between the eyebrows and is anchored in the carotid plexus in the vicinity of the pituitary gland, the master endocrine gland affecting all our hormonal functions, found at the base of the brain. Therefore, it affects our moods and behavior. The back side is at the back of the head.

Spokes
The energy undulates in such a manner as to give the appearance of ninety six spokes. The color of this center gives it the appearance of being divided in halves.

Age of Development
8 ½ to 14 years

Judgement That Blocks Energy
Confusion, I'm Opposite - This center is about clear seeing (clairvoyance), visions, imagination and other visually based abilities that enable us to see the future, plan for the future, and change whatever needs to be changed to reach it. Confusion muddles clear seeing and keeps

us grounded in the present. This center is also concerned with self-image and self-perception. It provides the means to change our view of self and the world in order to bring the self into alignment with the future. The decision, *"I'm opposite"* keeps us in opposition to our best interests by having us continually behave opposite from way from that is required for us to change and plan for the future.

Thought That Blocks Energy
Irritation - a mental state of annoyance that interprets behavior, actions, and events that don't flow as expected or that interrupt a series of activities or thoughts, as annoying. This mental state is antithetic to change in the present to bring ourselves into alignment with the future. It shows up in our life as a belief system that can be self-destructive, a self image that can be negative, and goals that can be opposite from our highest purpose.

Emotions That Block Energy
Antagonism - This is the predominate conscious emotion. Antagonism is active opposition. The internal opposition is against our realizing our potentials as a result of lack of

self-acceptance and low self-image. Specifically, we do not accept the clairvoyant visions and images that we receive of ourselves. Our behaviors are in active opposition to those images. Externally, we act in opposition to people, and situations that are supportive to us realizing our potentials. When pushed by people or events toward actions that would enable the realization of our highest goals, we profess, act and express confusion. Other emotions present that reflect our feelings about ourselves are shame, especially as we acknowledge the gap between our potential and our current actions; hopelessness as we experience the degree to which our belief system has us locked into low self esteem; and unexpressed resentment towards the people and events that push us to fulfill our potential.

Behavior When Energy is Blocked

People, situations, events get on your nerves. This is the intolerance to any interruption in the flow of your activities or your thoughts. This behavior keeps people at a distance and creates experiences of being misunderstood.

Physical Manifestation of Blocked Energy

Since this Chakra is linked to the pituitary gland, physical problems may manifest in all areas regulated by the hormones of the pituitary gland resulting in major or minor endocrine imbalances. Irritation can manifest in any area of the body as an eruption, ulcer or inflammatory response. Some examples are: skin irritations that reflect how we feel about ourselves; sinusitis, which reflects emotional irritation; shingles, which indicates a breakdown in communication with our divine self. Shingles affect the nerves and the nerves are the means of communication within ourselves. Eyesight issues; unwillingness to see, especially to see the future. The head holds our consciousness; any problems with the head reflects a relationship problem with our consciousness. Headaches indicate self dislike, irritation with ourselves, locking thoughts or feelings inside our head.

Healing Element

Water, actual water or the symbol of water.

Healing Musical Note

The key of G and the music of chimes, Tibetan bells, and crystal bowls. Sound OM.

Color

This Chakra has two colors: one half is rose- colored with some yellow in it and the other half is purplish-blue. The healing color is indigo (a deep purple) and emerald green.

Healing Breath Cycle

8 seconds: 4 seconds on the inhale and 4 seconds on the exhale.

Spiritual Goal

Focusing through the power of creative visualization. Clearly seeing our path and purpose.

Seeing a higher vision of ourselves and allowing ourselves to be drawn to and utilize opportunities that will manifest our Divine Self and our Divine Purpose.

God Conscious Decision

I'm certain of my path and purpose; God's creation pleasures me

Sixth Chakra Story

Allison was considered very bright by her teachers but had failing grades. She cut school a lot to hang out with the kids she considered hip. If they had marijuana or cocaine, she would smoke or sniff with them. She liked the way it made her feel, real mellow. Nothing irritated her when she was high. When she wasn't high, her parents telling her what to wear, and how to act, her teachers constantly harping on how bright she was and how she wasn't living up to her potential, really irritated her. She didn't feel she was that smart and she had the grades to prove it.

Seventh Chakra

Location

The seventh Chakra is referred to as the crown Chakra. The in-body, anchoring of it is at the top of the head in the area of the "soft spot." It is associated with the pineal gland. The remainder of the front side of the crown Chakra and the back side of the crown Chakra is located on higher planes. The crown Chakra is the access point of our consciousness and our spiritual existence.

Spokes

The energy undulates in such a manner as to give the appearance of nine hundred and sixty spokes.

Age of Development

14 to 21 years; this Chakra is fully activated at birth. The baby's soft spot is the entry point for spiritual energy.

Judgement That Blocks Energy

Life's a Struggle, God Doesn't Support Me - This center is our direct connection to the Creator. Spiritual energies enter through this Chakra feeding our spiritual development. When we are receptive, we receive the guidance needed to understand our purpose for being here on earth at this time. Through this center, we develop knowledge of our divinity, of our unity and unbroken continuity with God, unity with all our relations, and knowledge of principles in alignment with Divine laws allowing them to guide our life choices.

The judgement, " *Life's a Struggle, God Doesn't Support Me*" blocks receptivity to Divine guidance giving rise to struggle, disharmony, and lack of direction. It's a self fulfilling prophecy. Believing that God doesn't support us can lead to separation and individualism ruled by the ego's seeking power through relationships. Under ego's control, one believes that the end justifies the means. The judgement can also lead to fear of God and fear of Love.

Thought That Blocks Energy
Overload - a mental state of being overburdened. Life's activities are accomplished through the application of physical and mental labor, personal drive, and ego determination.

Emotion That Block Energy
No Sympathy - There is the inability to feel empathically what another person feels and to be affected with feelings similar to those of another person. The numbness generates alienation from others as well as from self, especially Divine self. No sympathy can play itself out in feeling like a victim who is doing all the work or it can play out in victimizing others . The emptiness of the spiritual connection drives the material. Work is viewed as the only meaning for living.

Behavior When Energy is Blocked
One of the predominate behaviors is that of being a workaholic. This is a person who is too busy for family, friends, vacations, fun, etc. They are very materially directed and seem to thrive on work. On the flip side is the person who is overwhelmed with life. What they are doing is too much for them, they can't handle it. Lack of self-understanding, lack of direction, ungrounded, and extreme insecurity are other behavioral manifestations.

Physical Manifestation of Blocked Energy
The physical problems that arise stem from the relationship of this center to the pineal gland and its function as a vehicle for spiritual energies, that sustain our spiritual development. Since the pineal gland is an immune system regulator, immune system disorders can occur. The blocking of spiritual energies also appear in the form of learning disabilities, mental illness, and sometimes alcoholism.

Healing Element
Earth, the actual earth or the symbol for earth.

Healing Musical Note
The note of E. Musical compositions with electronic synthesizers. Sound- MMM.
Healing Breath Cycle
Sixteen seconds, eight on the inhale and eight on the exhale.

Healing Color
The Chakra color is golden yellow and violet
Spiritual Goal
Unity with all life, with all spirits, expressing harmoniously our individuality with unity. Defining one's purpose within the grand dance of the universe. Being able to keep in balance one's movements with the whole dance.
God Conscious Decision
I Am expressing in all aspects of my life my vision of divine purpose; God supports me.
Seventh Chakra Story
Edwin is a workaholic, but you couldn't tell him that. He is a high powered CEO who has built a successful business. He has plenty of money but never has time to relax and spend time with his family. He feels that no one, especially his wife, has any sympathy or understanding for him, how hard he works and what it takes to keep on top with his business. In fact, there are times when he feels overwhelmed with the relationship demands of his family. He is a good provider, and why that's not enough for his wife escapes him. Certainly, they want for nothing that money can buy.
Eighth Chakra
Location
This is the first of the four out-of-body Chakras we will discuss in this book. The eighth Chakra is 1 to1 and ½ inches above the crown Chakra.

Spokes

The eighth Chakra does not have spokes; it exists as a whirling mass of energy, a plate like spiral vortex 1 to 1 and ½ inches above the crown Chakra . It is a portal in and through the time/space continuum giving us access to other dimensions.

Age of Development

This Chakra is fully activated at birth. From age 21 to 28, it comes into alignment. During these ages, our choices are governed by this Chakra. When this Chakra comes into alignment, it is an opportunity to clear other lives.

Judgement That Blocks Energy

I'm Stuck in the Past - This center is our direct connection to our sacred purpose. It is the Temple of Understanding within us where we have stored information on all our lives, the patterns, the learning, the relationships (Ywahoo, pg 106). It is also referred to as the Karma Chakra, giving us information about the issues we have come to resolve in this lifetime.

The judgement, *"I'm Stuck in the Past,"* keeps us repeating patterns and relationships that are not in harmony with our primary purpose in this lifetime. In the repetition of patterns and relationships, we are unable to affirm our current purpose by releasing and burning those old patterns so that we can move beyond them. Because this center also relates to time, time issues, such as being too late or too early, occur. Timing issues around when it is the appropriate time to do this, that, or the other thing also occur. When we are in harmony with our primary purpose in this lifetime, our timing is in alignment.

Thought That Blocks Energy

Independence - a mental state of seeking to not be influenced or controlled by others by thinking or acting for one self. The thought that the direction of our life is up to us, thus we experience ourselves as independent of our Creator. We do not allow guidance or support to be experienced denying our partnership with the divine mind.

Emotion That Blocks Energy

Fear - at the age this Chakra is activated, people are shedding parental supports, taking on "adult" responsibilities, and making choices about partners, careers, lifestyle, etc. There is apprehension around these choices as the unresolved other life feelings and beliefs surface. Yet, these are the conditions of our embodiment. We are here in a body to work them out, and we are offered the choice to change previous patterns of relationship as this Chakra is activated. There is fear around meeting our divine qualities as we learn to undo beliefs, feelings, and relationship patterns from other lives.

Behavior When Energy is Blocked

One of the predominate behaviors is opposition, opposition to what we judge as external attempts to control or influence us. What we are reexperiencing, in fact, are the old patterns surfacing for acknowledgment and release. We get caught up in the opposition. By fighting the illusion of influence and control, we wind up caught up in and repeating the relationship pattern of other lives that are co-existing in us, all the while believing we are acting independently and making new choices. Patterns that are not released when this Chakra is aligned continue to show up in our lives as chronic physical, emotional, spiritual, and relationship problems.

Physical Manifestation of Blocked Energy

Physical problems that appear are related to other lives that are co-existing.

Healing Element

Ether, Prana, or Chi

Healing Musical Note

B flat

Healing Breath Cycle
Twenty four seconds, twelve on the inhale and twelve on the exhale.

Healing Color
White and gold light. The eighth Chakra is an iridescent mother of pearl color.

Spiritual Goal
Full awareness of the lesson for this life and the learning we have embodied to learn. Greater awareness of our sacred purpose in this lifetime.

God Conscious Decision
I Am on purpose in this lifetime; I express my sacred purpose in a timely manner

Eighth Chakra Story
Margarette went away to college, and upon graduation, decided to settle in a city away from her parents. She felt that being near them would result in their attempt to control her life. As she settled into her chosen career, she noticed that she always felt that the people in authority at her job were unreasonably critical of her. There were times when she actually felt persecuted by them. Her co-workers told her she was overreacting, but she couldn't shake that feeling of persecution no matter how hard she tried. After about a year of this, she began to develop pains in her neck. She consulted several physicians but they could not find any physical cause for the neck pain.

The experience of persecution and the neck pain were related to a past life experience. In a Quantum Dynamic's Transformation Breath session Margaret was taken back to a past life time where she was persecuted and hung. The pattern was released for all life times. She was then able to utilize subsequent sessions to identify and release judgements, thoughts and emotions enabling her to step into her purpose in this life time and move through the lessons she had embodied to learn in this life time.

Location

Above the head, approximately one arm's length.

Spokes

The ninth Chakra does not have spokes. It exists as a funnel-shaped energy vortex one arms length above the head.

Age of Development

The ninth Chakra is the soul Chakra. It is the soul body containing the symbols, patterns and archetypes pertinent to a particular individual as well as the imprint or template for the physical body into which spirit will incarnate for meeting the soul's ends. As such, the soul Chakra is present prior to incarnation and helps select the appropriate sperm and egg for this particular individual's incarnation (Dale, pg 52). This is the Chakra that utilizes sexual energy in manifesting. The soul Chakra comes into alignment to open at age 28 to 35.

Judgement That Blocks Energy

Change Hurts or Kills- When this Chakra is brought into alignment, we are offered the opportunity to step into our sacred purpose. The alignment opening may be accompanied by major changes in our lives as we shed that which holds us from receiving knowledge of our self as spirit. When these major changes occur, we have a choice. We can cling to our life as we have known it and attempt to reconstruct that which has changed, or we can surrender. In surrendering, we are willing to clear the feelings that inhibit true expression of purpose, change the judgements that do not support the spirit self, and allow our life to be changed so that we can move forward towards acceptance of our sacred purpose.

The judgement, *"Change Hurts or Kills,"* holds us back from accepting the immense changes that are a prerequisite to moving forward as a spirit-in-person. It is a decision that abdicates responsibility for fulfillment of the purpose for which we incarnated. As our life unfolds, further opportunities are offered for us to embrace our purpose.

Thought That Blocks Energy

Intolerance- This is a mental state in which there is unwillingness or refusal to endure difference. The emerging true self is not tolerated.

Emotion That Blocks Energy

Fear- fear abounds as we perceive our world, as we have constructed it, coming apart. Fear is the absence of love. When we are presented with the opportunity to experience who we are, we are also presented with the opportunity to experience Love. When we embrace the opportunity, we move towards Love; when we don't, we remain in fear. We may experience emotional conflict as we sift through feelings that support and don't support our life's purpose.

Behavior When Energy is Blocked

One of the predominant behaviors is avoidance. This is a person who avoids examining beliefs, avoids feelings, avoids experiences that heighten awareness, avoids insight, avoids healing.

Physical Manifestation of Blocked Energy

We have the opportunity to heal the soul body so that we do not have to repeat our illness lessons over and over.

Healing Element

Love

Healing Musical Note

This is a very high vibrational energy center and does not have a musical note associated with it.

Healing Breath Cycle

Use a cycle of 24 seconds. 12 on the inhale and 12 on the exhale.

Healing Color

The color of the Chakra is gold. Gold light and white light.

Spiritual Goal
Acceptance of purpose.

God Conscious Decision
"I am all that I have been, I am all that I would be, I am all that I Am" (Byars), I have a true knowing of my gift and purpose at this time.

Ninth Chakra Story
Ebun was a doctoral student and Health Activist. She was sure of her opinions. She relied predominately upon her intellet and logic in coping with life. She was in the midst of a very intense struggle to keep Sydenham Hospital from closing and was using this struggle as research for her dissertation. One night after she went to bed, she awoke to the sounds of her front door crashing in and heard a male voice shout, "Come out with your hands up!" The NYC police had blocked off her street, and 50 FBI agents had entered her building in an illegal search. She was forcibly removed from her apartment, threatened, and physically searched. Her apartment was also searched. When that night of terror was finished, she held a press conference and filed a
lawsuit against the FBI. Filing of a lawsuit brought increased FBI surveillance and harassment. Her life was turned upside down. She was fearful, couldn't sleep, and couldn't do any of her school work. She was diagnosed with Post Traumatic Stress Syndrome. Ebun came unglued, engulfed as she was in unceasing emotions and thoughts. It was as if every thought and emotion that she had ever experienced was up for review. She surrendered. She challenged God to give her guidance or end her life. She began a fast, vowing not to eat and drink until she received guidance or die. On the seventh day of the fast, she had a vision.

Tenth Chakra

Location

One and one half to four feet under the feet.

Spokes

The tenth Chakra does not have spokes. It exists as an funnel-shaped energy vortex that grounds us. It releases wastes from the physical body and the Chakra and auric system into the earth for transformation and brings to these systems the elements needed (Dale, pg 54).

Age of Development

Preconception and conception; comes into alignment to open at 35 to 42 years. The tenth Chakra is activated before conception to gather energy from pre existing lives, our parent's existence and the ancestural background to enable us to meet the physical, mental, emotional, and spiritual challenges we will face once we are embodied.

Judgement That Blocks Energy

It's Painful to Be Fully Here- When this Chakra is brought into alignment, we have the opportunity to fully incarnate or fully bring into our body our spiritual self. The tenth Chakra contains memories and feelings of our previous lives, our ancestral memories, energies and information that we need for everyday life. The power, wisdom, nurturing, and sustenance gained from these collective experiences surface through the tenth Chakra. We have the opportunity to apply this knowledge and sustenance to the lessons presented to us in this lifetime as these lessons are the ones we are here to overcome. Fully grounding our spiritual self or our true identity enables us to develop a purposeful lifestyle to accomplish the lessons of this lifetime and carry out our life's purpose. The judgement, *"It's Painful to be Fully Here,"* has several consequences. We are frightened of our true self, judge it as bad, and suppress its emergence. This results in lack of personal power that leaves us ungrounded, spaced out, lacking the full integration of all the true components of our self, the very components that were specifically selected by our soul to assist us to accomplish our life goals. A second consequence is shutting down this Chakra. Shutting down occurs when the events, feelings, and energies to which we are connected through the tenth Chakra are too painful. This Chakra provides and maintains the influx of energy necessary for "fight or flight" to deal with life's scary situations or dangers. Shutting down this energy channel leaves us lacking the physical and emotional resiliency to effectively cope and master the scary situations we encounter. Finally, as a result of the judgement, as we encounter situations that are our lessons for this lifetime, we may suppress our negative feelings, blocking the energy of this Chakra. We effectively cut ourselves off from the power, wisdom, nurturing, and sustenance of previous experiences. This may show up in our life as repressed memories, dissociation, lack of personal power, low energy, and lack of enthusiasm for life.

Thought That Block Energy
Disconnected - This is a mental state in that the connection, communication, and agreement to fully incarnate is interrupted or severed.

Emotion That Block Energy
Fear - Especially inappropriate use of the "fight or flight" response. The smallest situation is blown up into its worse possible conclusion. Because we are not grounded we feel helpless and unable to cope. Fear keeps us from realizing our hopes and dreams, goals and aspirations.

Behavior When Energy Is Blocked
This is an ungrounded person. They are spaced out, lack focus, insecure, out of touch with their feelings and needs. They are vulnerable physically and/or psychically and may experience abuse in either of these areas from

people and/or spirits. They have difficulty coping with the vicissitudes of everyday life and with stress.

Physical Manifestation of Blocked Energy
Stress related problems such as infections, hypertension; weight problems because the mind layers the body with tissue in an attempt to ground it and help the individual to feel secure;

avoidance of feelings, decisions, commitments; foot, ankle and leg problems. Our feet transport information from our past lives, and we take our stance to fight or flee with our feet. Our legs transport information from our ancestor lineage. Problems in these areas are a result of the disconnect and the blockage of energy. Psychiatric problems such as schizophrenia, dissociated states, and psychosis.

Healing Element
Earth, air, fire and water. The symbols or the actual elements.

Healing Musical Note
A, A# and C. Music using deep low drums or the bassoon

Healing Color
The color of the Chakra is earth tones, including citron, brown, mauve, russet, limestone, yellow, olive green, and obsidian. The healing color is pink and peach.

Healing Breath Cycle
16 seconds, 8 on the inhale and 8 on the exhale.

Spiritual Goal
Grounding of our soul, our true self; our spiritual self.

God Conscious Decision
I am fully here, able to cope; I am expressing my divine purpose in a grounded, practical way and enjoying life.

Chakra Story
Jeanne was a actress just beginning her career. She knew she wanted to act but had difficulty getting to auditions, staying focused on a character, and rehearsing parts for

auditions. In addition, her agent told her she needed a stage name, but she couldn't make up her mind. One month she would use one name and the next month she would use another. It got hard keeping up with the names. Sometimes she felt she had three or four people within her all vieing to be named as the permanent name and person.

She rented a floor in a brownstone and was very intimidated by the landlord who would come into her room in her absence and move her things around. She had a history of sexual abuse when she was a child, and the relationship with the landlord evoked memories of that experience. She was paralyzed with fear and unable to think clearly about how to handle the situation.

She went to a practitioner for help with these problems. At first she felt she was getting some assistance, then she began to feel that this man was manipulating her mind psychically. This came to a head one night when he was in her dreams, and she felt as if he was in the bed touching her.

Eleventh Chakra
Location
Around the hands and feet, especially the palmar surface of the hands and the feet.
Spokes
The eleventh Chakra does not have spokes, it is a pink film around the hands and the feet (Dale, pg106).
Age of Development
Birth. Continues to grow in sensitivity, especially in people who use their hands consciously for energy work. When developed from conscious healing work, it gives off a blue and white glow.

Judgement That Blocks Energy
I Can't Handle Life - Development of this Chakra is
development of our ability to bring in energy and use it as
well as the ability to release energy our body no longer
needs. It also relates to our willingness to touch and be
touched, to receive and to give, to hold and to let go. To
stand and be grounded in life secure in the direction we
are traveling. The judgement, *"I Can't Handle Life,"* is a
judgement affecting our entire being. Shut down in this
Chakra blocks the energy exchange and keeps us holding
on to energetic waste that should be discharged from the
body. Holding onto energetic waste that effects the in-
body Chakras below the heart Chakra, imbalancing us so
that we lack a firm grasp on the material world.

Thought That Block Judgement
Withdrawal - A mental state of pulling back by removing
oneself from participation. The with- holding of full
physical, mental, and emotional participation in life.

Emotion That Block Energy
Shut Down - Withholding emotional energy by closing
off the interchange. Pulling back from touching and being
touched.

Behavior When Energy is Blocked
*This person can appear shallow, listless, lacking in
vitality.* They may also be spaced-out and unable to deal
with the practical day-to-day demands of the material
world, unsure of direction and insecure.

Physical Manifestation Of Blocked Energy
Problems with the hands or feet and the lower
extremities.

Healing Element
Love, Prana

Healing Musical Note
Unknown

Healing Color
White and gold

Healing Breath Cycle
Unknown
Spiritual Goal
Continuous energy interchange.
God Conscious Decision
I fully participate in life's exchanges.
Eleventh Chakra Story
Don is an accountant. He enjoys his work and is highly
praised by his employer. He is shy and has fantasies about
relationships with women but finds relationships with real
women difficult to sustain. The women dated in the past
complained that he is cold and distant, and broke off the
relationship after a few months. The fantasy relationships
always work out better. Recently his feet and legs have
been feeling cold and numb. He's seen several doctors
who have tested his circulation and found nothing wrong.

Chapter Two Summary

1. Chakras are the integrating energy systems holding the pattern of the physical body, the auric fields, the celestial connection and the material form for manifesting and melds these energies together as a definite unique living organism.

2. There are seven in-body Chakras and four out-of body Chakras.

3. The seven in-body Chakras have spokes and are anchored to the spine surfacing at the front and the back of the physical body.

4. The four out-of -body Chakras link the material slower elemental energies with the spiritual higher frequency celestial energies.

5. Our state of consciousness influences the vibratory rate of the Chakras impacting what we receive, transmit and manifest.

6. Judgements, thoughts and emotions which are reflective of our state of consciousness can block the optimal functioning of the Chakras and their ability to sustain growth, development and healing.

The South

The warmth of the South wind enables the seeds of regeneration of self to be planted and to grow forth as the three sisters: Wisdom, Will and Love. Wisdom gathers experience and recognizes responsibility. Will fosters the consciousness of purpose and direction, and Love gives sustenance to the regenerated self.

Chapter Three
Creating Separation, Upset and Designing Disease

Master the sacred body this temple built by your thoughts.
This body is an opportunity. It belongs not to your self alone
but to all those with whom you interact. It is a gift, given and
earned through your actions, to express the beauty of Creation
in this time.
Dhyani Ywahoo, <u>Voices of Our Ancestors</u>

The Body and the Mind

We are truly Spirit animating a magnificent
organized electro-magnetic energy system called the
Body. The Body is a learning device of the Mind. It is a
manifestation of our consciousness. Its purpose is to
facilitate learning.

In our identification with the dense physical body,
we separate the physical part of ourselves from the
totality of our magnificent energy system. We hear with
the physical body's ears, we touch with its skin surface,
perceive with its eyes unaware that these are limited
perceptions and as such, limit our awareness. Keeping our
awareness limited to the physical body, we are unaware
of our Chakras, our auric fields and the processes that
enable us to maintain health or create disease.   The
dense physical body enables us to experience the
physical/material world and in this sense it cannot be
denied, but to overvalue it and assign creative powers to it
is an error. When we say things like, "My back aches,"
"My stomach developed an ulcer" or "I caught a cold" we
are attributing the result, which is the back ache, the
stomach ulcer, etc, that our consciousness has created in
the body, to the body. Most of us would not say, "I
created an ache in my back," "I created an ulcer in my
stomach," or "I created a cold." Yet, that is precisely

what has happened. Our consciousness creates changes in our body. The thoughts we hold, the words we repeatedly use, the interactions we create, the actions we take, our feeling states and emotions have all created our body up to this point. What we choose to think, say, do and feel now, in this moment, is creating our body tomorrow. The point of power for creation is always in the current moment. Catch your thought, survey your consciousness right now. Do you want the thought you are thinking right now to become your experience? Do you want the thought you are thinking right now to show up in your body? Thought creates. Thought is energy. Matter is slowed down energy. Thought forms matter.

When I took my first Quantum Dynamics workshop and was first introduced to this concept that thought is creative, I rejected it. I decided that this was just a way to blame the victim. After all, I was a nurse, I had seen the full range of physical disease and could not believe that anyone would think that up to create for themselves. As a health activist, the implications of accepting the concept that our thoughts create disease in our bodies in terms of society frightened me. I felt the policy implications of the concept could justify government withdrawing it's responsibility for third party payment for the treatment of illness. I also felt that the concept denied environmental pollution's contribution to disease. On the other hand, working in psychiatry had developed in me a respect for the power of the mind. I had repeated demonstrations in working with my clients that you can change experiences and physical problems by changing thoughts. Additionally, there was considerable research documenting examples of the mind's power over the body. I was willing to use the process to see if it worked for me. I certainly had no other options at the time.

In using the process, I began to experience the powerful implications of the concept that my thoughts are creative. If I can create, then I can change, not only myself but my environment. As a political activist, I did not have to remain a minority, subject to the vicissitudes of racism and sexism. I began to experience that changing my consciousness and assisting others to do the same made a difference.

Our Belief in Separation

We are very used to the idea of matter or mass being converted into energy, wood burning produces heat.... energy. The converse is also true that energy can be converted into mass, the last and most famous aspect of the special theory of relativity that mass is a form of energy and that energy has mass. The wood that we burn in the fire is comprised of wood fibers, which are actually patterns of cells. Under magnification the cells are patterns of molecules. Under higher magnification the molecules, are patterns of atoms, and the atoms are patterns of subatomic particles, subatomic particles the ultimate stuff of matter that is pure energy. Therefore, mass is energy and energy is mass. Energy is everywhere and incessantly assuming first this form then that form. Our body is energy assuming a particular form that was first assembled by our mother's consciousness and is maintained by our consciousness--Mind.

We have a higher Mind that is joined with God. It is the spiritual self. We have a lower mind that is the home of the ego/the human self/intellect. When the lower mind dominates, acting as if it is the highest authority, we are into separation. We then separate the physical from the emotional, the mental from the emotional, and the spiritual from the mental, emotional and physical. We perceive only the physical body. In doing this, we present an narrow view of ourselves that doesn't reflect our inner most feelings and thoughts, the radiant beauty of our Body, or our God Presence. In our most extreme form of denial, we think we live within the physical body and die when it does. We use the physical body to separate ourselves from Love; we think we are safe from Love in the body. We use the physical body to separate Love from sex and to separate sex from God's Light. In the physical body, we feel safe from Love, Light, emotions, spirit, and thoughts. We identify with the physical body, cling to it, worship it. Just glance at the magazines in the supermarket, that reflect our concern with the physical body. We regard ourselves as what we have identified with as our safety. We use it to keep ourselves from charting the unknown possibilities of existence. We remain in the body keeping Light and Love outside by denying the rest of our energy system. We allow the ego/mind/intellect to use the physical body as a weapon of exclusion, a demonstration of separateness. And we are convinced that the body can act like the Mind, that it can create. We are convinced that the body is self sufficient, that it is separate from God.

We think the body is self motivated and independent, unaware that it responds only to the intentions of the Mind. The body cannot create, the Mind creates. The body displays this creation. If we want to know what we are thinking, look at the body. The body form is shaped by consciousness. If we want to change the body, we have to change the mind, if we what to heal the body, we have to change the mind.

The belief that the body creates physical illness rests on the belief that there is creative ability in matter that consciousness/Mind cannot control. We see illness as something fixed, a condition or state of the body. The more we perceive it in that way, the more matter we create in the form of illness. Illness is a messenger, carrying information about an imbalance within our energy system. This imbalance created by the mind/ego/intellect, is emotional, mental and spiritual. It is all three because we cannot separate these aspects. An imbalance is the result of a block in energy flow in any of the eleven energy centers described in the previous chapter. A block obstructs or impedes the passage of energy. Remember, we spoke about the synchronous nature of the Chakras and how a block in the flow of energy of one creates an imbalance in all Chakras. In my experience, judgement is always at the root of an imbalance.

Creating Upset

A judgement is a decision that we make about a situation or an event. It is the mental act of evaluation through comparison or contrast. Judgements made from sensory perceptions are fallible. These judgements are a crystallization of belief patterns that are out-pictured in our experiences. "A belief is a point of conscious energy pulsating to a certain vibration within the sphere of its own realm of possibility/probability"(Price, pg 64). For example, Pat calls up an acquaintance/coworker, leaves a message on the machine but the co-worker doesn't return her call. Pat can decide that s/he doesn't like her and this is s/he hasn't returned her call, or Pat can decide that s/he doesn't think she's important and emotionally feel rejected by the person. These decisions are judgements being made about the event of the unreturned phone call. These judgements are attached to the feeling state of love or fear which in turn brings forth an emotion--feeling rejected or not loved. Pat is now upset. An event + a judgement = an upset. But the feeling rejected or not loved did not begin with the event. A belief pattern

73

already existed. In her mind, Pat believes she is unworthy and unloved, and that belief did not begin with this particular situation. Nor is the feeling of rejection new to this situation. These are old patterns, crystallized belief patterns that are out pictured in the experience of an unreturned phone call. The upset is a messenger: "Hey look, you feel unworthy; you feel unloved," be with the situation; give yourself time to find out what it means. Price indicates that there are varying degrees of belief with the externalization reflecting the exact degree (Price, pg 64). For example, one hundred percent belief, one hundred percent out picturing of experiences of rejection; fifty percent belief fifty percent out picturing of experiences of rejection and so on.

The belief of rejection blocks to varying degrees out pictured experiences of receiving and giving unconditional Love. There is only one film being projected on the screen of life's experience entitled, "I'm Unlovable; Unworthy of God's Love," Two energies cannot occupy the same space at the same time, so when the belief "I'm unlovable unworthy of God's Love" is on life's screen, the ability to receive and give Love is absent to the degrees of the belief. Love is what sustains us in synchronous balance as an open energy system. The current situation presented Pat with an opportunity to see the judgement, and if she sees the judgement, she might also see the core belief pattern. Pat's belief pattern is judging interpersonal situations where people do not respond as she desires them to as rejection. What film is being projected on your screen of life?

Core beliefs are made very early in life, as early as the birthing experience. In the framework of Quantum Dynamics there are eleven core beliefs, which are outlined in the second chapter as the **"Judgement that**

blocks energy." I will summarize them here. Each summarized belief corresponds to a Chakra as follows:

I'm wrong, I'm right, They're wrong - First Chakra
Aliveness Hurts or Kills - Second Chakra
Unworthy to Receive- Third Chakra
I'm Not Enough, I'm Too Much - Fourth Chakra
I'm Unlovable, Unworthy of God's Love- Fifth Chakra
Confusion I'm Opposite- Sixth Chakra
Life's a Struggle, God Doesn't Support Me- Seventh Chakra
I'm Stuck in the Past - Eight Chakra
Change Hurts or Kills - Ninth Chakra
It's Painful to be Fully Here - Tenth Chakra
I Can't Handle Life - Eleventh Chakra.

The first seven judgements are bottom line core beliefs identified by the rebirthing movement as a result of rebirthing hundreds of thousands of people. I have identified the latter four based on my Quantum Dynamics work with people. We can have one or more predominant judgements or all eleven.

Creating Separation

When ego/intellect/mind is in charge, we are in separation. Separation occurs at two levels, original separation and birth separation. Original separation took place over a period of millions of years and involves two aspects: beliefs we hold as manifested spirits that we created ourselves; and fear we have created about holding the first belief.

God extended Him/Her self to us as His/Her creations, giving us the loving will and ability to create. When we use our ability to create, we are co-creators with God since we are one with God. In our ability to create,

74

we are like our Creator. But we did not create ourselves. The original creation of ourselves as spirits is the only sense in which God and God's creations, us, are not co-creators. We did not generate the life that created us as manifesting spirits and we do not generate the life that sustains us. We must receive life from God or we cannot live. We can perceive ourselves as self creating, we can perceive ourselves as separate, but we cannot do more than believe it. We cannot make it true (Original Cause, pg x).

Every culture has a creation mythology that includes a myth about original separation. In the Judeo-Christian culture it is the story about Adam and Eve and eating the forbidden fruit from the Tree of Knowledge, which is a symbolic expression for usurping the ability for self creating. The tree symbolizes a dual state of consciousness creation and mis-creation. The belief in separation is a miscreation of the mind. It is a powerful, very real, very fearful, destructive system of thought and in opposition to our God consciousness. We are the author of fear. We have chosen to create unlike the Creator. We have made fear for ourselves. We have used our power of creation to create fear filled experiences. When confronted with a horrendous situation we sometimes ask, "Why did God let this happen?" That question abdicates our creative responsibility for the world as we have miscreated it. The question we ought to ask is "How did I participate in creating this?"

When I first began to appreciate that my thoughts create, I stopped watching the news because I responded to the continuous stream of murder and mayhem with anger at the aggressor, blame at society, and judgements. I realized that none of these responses were helpful and only served to give more energy to the collective consciousness that miscreated murder and mayhem. Now, I consciously watch the news once a week, and I process myself on the judgements and emotions being reflected by the news stories. I have thoughts of forgiveness for the aggressor and send light and love to all situations of distress. The fundamental conflict in this world is between creation and miscreation. All fear is implicit in miscreation, all Love is implicit in creation.

The second level of separation, birth separation, occurs when we are born into the material world into a Body. This level of separation involves denial. There are two levels of denial: denial of Light and Love in the sexual act and the emotional denials adults are holding when they engage in sex. The denial of Light and Love in the sexual act means that we view sex as physical only, or dirty, something to be done in the dark. We do not view sex as sacred, an action in which God's Light and Love are present. Many of us have been taught that sex has no place in worshiping God. As adults we may be denying anger, denying love, intimacy or pain while we are engaged in sex.

Sexual energy is magnetic. Magnetic energy attracts what it is vibrating to. This is the magnetic force of desire. Denial attracts denial. If there is no light, then there is darkness. The presence of denial in the sexual act, the energy of which the ninth Charka uses enabling the manifesting spirit to incarnates into a Body, combined with the placing of sexuality outside the presence of God's Light and Love results in the birthing process acting like a blow to the head of the incarnating spirit. Being born in the presence of denial and darkness, lowers our consciousness. The eighth, ninth, and tenth Charka are present at conception and birth. Remember, the eighth Chakra is our direct connection to our sacred purpose, the ninth is the soul Chakra enabling us ro fulfill the purpose for which we incarnated, and the tenth enables us to meet the physical, mental, emotional and spiritual challenges we face as embodied spirits. We, therefore, forget who we are, we forget why we incarnated and forget the tools to overcome life's challenges. In the presence of darkness, experiencing separation, because God's Light and Love has been held apart from the sexual experience, we make a judgement about the experience. When we are in separation, we miscreate. Eventually, some of us remember and undo those denials and judgements, and some of us don't.

Miscreating Disease

Disease is a miscreation of the mind. In separation, our thoughts and our beliefs combine to miscreate imbalance in the physical, mental, emotional, and spiritual bodies; through the imbalance in the Chakras. There is a chain of events, a cause and an effect. There is a core judgement and a recurrent thought associated with that judgement that is the cause, and the event is the effect. The event might be a situation or disease. Let's examine how this works using the core judgement, "I'm wrong, I'm right, They're wrong". In a situation where we make a mistake and someone approaches us about it, the process is, "I'm wrong but I want to be right, my survival depends on being right and they are trying to make me wrong but they're wrong." In reacting to that situation we are going to block out or obstruct any information that could possibly indicate that we were wrong. Deep in our subconscious we have these thoughts and have judged ourselves as wrong. That judgement, which we do not want to acknowledge, shows up in our world as a mistake.

This is when we experience anger. We get angry and will argue that we didn't make a mistake. We're going to show them that we're right, that we're perfect, that we don't make mistakes, any thing to avoid experiencing ourselves as wrong. We get angry, avoid, get stuck, all to deny our thoughts and core judgement of ourselves as wrong. We are upset, and when we are upset, we are caught up in our cycle of miscreation (See figure 4)

Figure 4

Cycle of Miscreation

Thought / belief/ judgement - Out pictured event-

Judgement- Emotions- Behaviors .

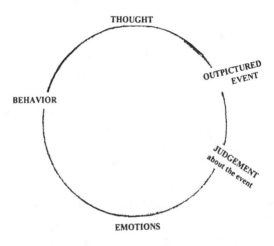

This cycle is recurrent. It is repeated over and over. Until we are aware of our own thoughts and core judgements, we blame others. When we become aware of our thoughts, core judgements, and feelings, we can break the cycle before the physical manifestation occurs. We can break the cycle and heal the energy bodies before a structural change occurs manifesting itself as illness in the physical body. The cycle of miscreation **Thought/ Belief/ Judgement -Out pictured Event-Judgement-Emotions-Behaviors** is replaced with a cycle of Creation. The cycle of creation involves: Awareness/release - Forgiveness/release-Acceptance/release --Thought- Out pictured event- Emotions- Behaviors (See figure 5).

Figure 5

Awareness/release -Forgiveness/release-
Acceptance/release --Thought- Out pictured event-
Emotions- Behaviors

Cycle of Miscreation

Cycle of Creation

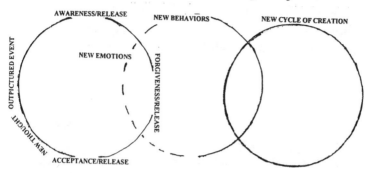

The cycle of creation spirals out, clearing our mental, emotional and spiritual bodies. In the awareness phase, we realize or become conscious of our miscreations. Becoming conscious of our miscreations begins with an awareness that perhaps there is another way of viewing a particular situation in which we have made a judgement. We become willing to see that situation in a different way. We also begin to recognize that this experience always happens to us and wonder why. We notice that we are always experiencing ourselves as wrong.

We use the first sister, Wisdom, to acknowledge and take responsibility for our miscreations. In the forgiveness phase, we forgive ourselves for what we have miscreated. We use the second sister, Will, to bring forth a consciousness of purpose and direction. We are willing to change our perception. We are willing to bring our core judgement out of the darkness. In the acceptance phase, we utilize the third sister, Love. We look with Love upon all we have miscreated. We withdraw our belief in our miscreationed core jugement. Our miscreations without belief no longer exist. In Light and Love, with faith and will, we create another belief. We imagine a new thought. We realize that thought and belief in consciousness. We continue to release the old beliefs as they surface. The new thoughts and beliefs are out pictured, enabling us to respond to situations with a different set of emotions, a different set of behaviors, and without judgement. We are able to increasingly experience Love and give Love. We end the separation from our loving Selves and from our Creator.

Getting the Message

Currently we believe that disease is caused by a germ, bacteria or virus that enters the body for various reasons such as a lowered immune system response. The body is unable to combat the virus and disease manifests. In the current western theory of disease, we have a structural change such as hardening of the arteries or narrowing of the lumen of the blood vessels that are related to diet and exercise, or we have inherited a disease, such as sickle cell anemia or a family pattern of cancer. Other disease, such as neurological degenerative diseases like Multiple Sclerosis, and Parkinson's Disease, a causative factor, has yet to be identified by western medicine although the pathophysiology of the disease can be described. To some degree, the current theory of disease allows us to work in a way to prevent disease by keeping our immune system functioning at a high level or by eating to avoid hi cholesterol foods, or getting checked on a regular basis to detect the early formation of cancer, etc. It doesn't allow us, however to understand why, despite all our work, we still manifest a cold, asthma, a stroke, or a heart attack. And it doesn't take into consideration the power of thought and emotions to produce form. The outer expression, disease, is a direct expression of our inner experience. As mentioned before, disease is the message. We must learn to understand the language of the message to get the meaning.

Our Bodies reflect the energy imbalances but we have not been taught to access the subtle and delicate ways that those imbalances show us what is happening to us. Our knowledge of the Charas discussed in Chapter Two are the road maps or the dictionary to understanding the message our Mind is sending us. If you have the map, we can decipher the message and see what the Body is showing us, what is happening to us. Deciphering the message does not eliminate seeking appropriate medical attention but enables you to augment that treatment.

The Mind uses the body symbolically to communicate manifesting illness, disease, and accidents as messages. With the map, you can read the message. If you don't have the map, you are lost and may assign all sorts of inaccurate meanings to what's going on with your body. For me, it was a very empowering moment when I realized that I AM covered by this robe of energy substance, that I AM creating the form, and that I AM able to change the form.

Decoding the Message

First, remember that the Charas have a front and back side. Pain, discomfort, and disease that manifest on the front side of the body are related to day-to-day reality, situations that we are currently facing. The front side of our body also reflects issues that are conscious or close to the surface even though we may choose to not acknowledge them. Pain, discomfort, and disease that manifest on the back side pertains to what we have put behind, i.e., the unconscious, past experiences, past lives.

Second, remember that there is a left and right side to the body. The left side of the body is controlled by the

81

right side of the brain; representing the feminine principle. It is magnetic, receptive, intuitive, non- linear, experience-based, caring, nurturing, and creative. It is the inner world of feelings and fantasy. Pain, disease and discomfort on the left side are indicative of issues around the expression of the feminine principle. It can also indicate issues around relationships with women, yourself (if you are a woman), mother, daughter, sister, female friends or relationships. The right side of the body is controlled by the left side of the brain; representing the masculine principle. It is electric, aggressive, assertive, linear, deductive, analytical, authoritative, and organizing. Pain, disease and discomfort on the right side of the body reflects issues with the expression of the masculine principle. It can also indicate relationship issues with men, yourself (if you are a male), father, brother, son, male friends or relationships.

The third factor to be taken into consideration is time and the physical manifestation of disease. It takes six to twelve months for a front side vibrational change created by a thought to manifest at the physical level. Prior to manifestation at the physical level, changes are occurring in the auric field corresponding to the Chakra whose vibration is impacted by the thought. Back side issues do not have a particular time frame. They can extend back to childhood or past lives and are being manifested now in order that we resolve them. Generally, when an issue manifests itself, it is time for it to be released. Energetically, the thought has changed, reached some resolution, and the Mind is ready to change the outward manifestation or outer miscreation.

The fourth, consideration is the proximity of the physical manifestation to a Chakra. Look at the Chakra nearest the site of the dysfunction. Generally, the energy in the Chakra nearest to the site of the dysfunction is blocked due to a judgement. In my experience, when there is a blockage in one Chakra, the Chakra above it and below it are also affected and out of balance. This occurs because an imbalance in the vibration of one Chakra impacts adjacent Chakras.

Let us use the example of stomach pain, experienced on the front left side of the abdomen. Applying our tools for decoding, because it is experienced on the front side it related to a recent experience associated with the third Chakra solar/lunar plexus reflecting issues of worthiness, personal power, achievement, and following intuition or inner knowing. On the left side, the expression of our personal power in a feminine way or in the presence of females, or judgements about females are blocking our expression of personal power. Since the pain is in the stomach, we begin to examine issues around digesting opinions and judgements from others that contribute to our feeling unworthy, expressing personal power or following our intuition. In this illustration, the second Chakra, located below the third Chakra, in the genital area relates to the expression of feelings and creativity. Since the second Chakra is affected, we would also look at expression of feelings and creativity in the area of personal power and achievement. The Chakra above the third, the fourth Chakra the heart, relates to love-- - love of self. Therefore, we begin to explore acceptance of ourselves and our desires in the areas of personal power, achievement, etc. Then take into consideration what upsets (event+judgement) have occured in the past six months to a year. When I counsel clients I use this system to decode symptoms enabling clients to reach a deeper level of clearing of issues.

Basically, there are four things being decoded: 1) Is the discomfort front side or back side? 2) Is it left or right side? 3) In which Chakra area is the dysfunction located?, 4) What is the time lapse between the upset and the appearance of the symptom?. When a physical symptom, repetitive experience or upset occurs, identify a Chakra, then ask yourself, "What is the judgement, the feeling or emotion blocking my energy here?" The judgement is generally unconscious. The feeling or emotion may not be easily identified since most of us are out of touch with our emotions and in denial of our feelings. When you locate the discomfort look at the chart in Chapter two, then you can identify which Chakra is out of balance, and by following the chart identify the judgement and emotions. Another way to identify the judgement is to examine your behavior and compare it to the chart. Most people are aware of their behavior. If the behavior fits the description for that Chakra, even if you are not aware of the emotions and judgement, assume that all else is correct. And if you're in denial of your behavior, ask a family member or friend to tell you.

Emotional Vibration and Disease

The questions that always arise for me in understanding disease are: "Why do certain people miscreate certain diseases?" and "Why does it occur in a particular organ ?" The answers to these questions have come to me through my work with radionics, radionics is a healing art based on universal laws. Radionics recognizes that each person is a unique combination of energies and that every substance that exists is composed of energy--light and vibration. Radionics uses certain instruments to focus thought. A thought is encoded as a vibratory rate on a paper card or a instrument's setting which replicates the vibratory pattern for a specific thing. That vibratory rate carries a coded vibration that can be transferred to another substance or a person through the focus of the instrument. Transmission to a person reminds him/her of what to do to bring about changes that will balance the disharmony. This concept is no different from the concept that information can be zapped from one computer to the next on an infrared beam.

Through radionics, I began to understand that emotions have different vibratory rates. This assisted me in understanding the concept of ranking emotions in Quantum Dynamics on a scale of emotional tones. Those emotions with the lower vibratory rate are at the bottom of the scale, and those with the higher vibrations are at the top of the scale. At the bottom of the Quantum Dynamics scale of emotional tones is total failure, at the top of the scale is serenity of beingness. "These emotional tones represent amount of flow or lack of flow of energy through the emotional body that a person is willing to allow" (Dvorak).The numbers next to each emotion represent one of the in body Chakras impacted by that emotional energy flow or lack of flow.

Scale of Emotional Tones
Jim Dvorak

7 SERENITY OF BEINGNESS
6 POSTULATES
2 GAMES
5 ACTION
1 EXHILARATION
3 AESTHETIC
4 ENTHUSIASM

7 CHEERFULNESS
6 STRONG INTEREST
2 CONSERVATION
5 MILD INTEREST
1 CONTENTED
3 DISINTERESTED
4 BOREDOM

7 MONOTONY
6 ANTAGONISM
2 HOSTILITY
5 PAIN
1 ANGER
3 HATE
4 RESENTMENT

7 NO SYMPATHY
6 UNEXPRESSED RESENTMENT
2 COVERT HOSTILITY
5 ANXIETY
1 FEAR
3 DESPAIR
4 TERROR

7 NUMB
6 SYMPATHY
2 PROPITIATION
5 GRIEF
1 MAKING AMENDS
3 UNDESERVING
4 SELF ABASEMENT

7 VICTIM
6 HOPELESS
2 APATHY
5 USELESS
1 DYING
3 BODY DEATH
4 FAILURE

7 PITY
6 SHAME
2 ACCOUNTABLE
5 BLAME
1 REGRET

3 CONTROLLING BODIES
4 PROTECTING BODIES

7 OWNING BODIES
6 APPROVAL FROM BODIES
2 NEEDING BODIES
5 WORSHIPING BODIES
1 SACRIFICE
3 HIDING
4 BEING OBJECTS

7 BEING NOTHING
6 CAN'T HIDE
2 TOTAL FAILURE

Start with serenity of beingness and stop at monotony
these fifteen are the emotions with a higher vibration.
Emotions beginning with antagonism on down to the end
of the list have a lower vibratory rate. These lower
vibratory emotions are associated with a judgement. The
judgement, the recurrent thought associated with that
particular belief, and the associated emotional component
create repeated disharmonious vibratory frequencies in
our electro-magnetic energy Body. A disharmonious
vibratory frequency is a frequency with a combination of
wave lengths that are discordant with the wave lengths
of our electro-magnetic energy system. A discordant
vibration breaks the conservation and distribution of vital
Love energy in the Body. Thus, the continuous
interchange of energy between our Body and God is
interrupted. When you listen to a radio and the signal is
interrupted, you hear static.

Recurrent thoughts, associated emotions, and
judgements create static. The black spots that appear in
the auric field or the color changes that occur are

indicative of that imbalance, that disruption. These signs are the static, so to speak. The black spots are an energy vacuum where light cannot escape. The color changes reflect the wave length of the discordant emotionor emotionally charged thoughts that exist as distinct energy or thought forms as named by Besant and Leadbeater. These thought forms can be seen by clairvoyant (clear vision) individuals who describe them as having shapes and colors. Color is the light reflected by an object, and in this case the light reflected by our auric field in the presence of a disharmonious emotion's wave length. When the continuous interchange of energy between self and God is interrupted we experience discomfort, stress, disease. The state of our health is proportionally relative to the balance between the reception of vital Love energy into our electro-magnetic Body and the distribution of that energy to the physical material that makes up the protoplasmic substance of our cells.

Where Disease Begins

When a thought/belief/judgement are manifesting disease, it can be intuitively observed as an energetic change in the auric energy system before there is a structural change in the physical body. For example: "Sickly yellow, slightly white energy in the prostate area, and white, yellow,and grey splotches between the second and third auric layers [emotional body and mental body] are indications of prostate cancer" (page 280, Dale). Disease begins first in the Auric field that reflects the imbalance, which auric field that is depends upon the judgement. Remember that each auric field is integrative, communicative and self regulating with a Chakra. The judgement impacts the Chakra by changing the vibration of the Chakra. The auric field integrated with the Chakra impacted by that judgement will manifest the energetic change first.

Our consciousness influences our electro-magnetic energy body and eventually our denser physical body because emotions and thoughts have magnetic properties. Most of us are familiar with the fact that if we hold a magnet over iron filings, we can change the shape of the iron filings, i.e., we can move them around into different shapes. The energy of human thoughts and feelings also have magnetic properties, that attract substances in vibrational harmony with the the thought or feeling. Remember the discussion about Pat and her co-worker's phone call? The magnetic properties also repel substances that are not in vibrational harmony with the the thought or feeling, just as a magnet harmonizes with iron and repels other metals not in harmony with it.

In order for illness to manifest, there must be a vibrational change sustained by an a thought, emotion, and a judgement. When a lowered vibrational change occurs, the Body's auric fields adapt, but cumulative interference imposes deviation, affecting the natural integrative, self regulating, communicative functions of the system, and subsequently a new way of organizing energy occurs i.e., the vibatory rate of the spiritual field is lowered. It is the trough repeatedly meeting the crest. This steps down to the etheric field and we may experience a symptom, which is the expression of friction. A symptom is indicative of the conflict between our illuminated consciousness, which strives to maintain wholeness and the lowered vibration's "imposed" deviation. Gradually, the friction becomes much more acute and the symptom changes into a state of being we call disease. The vibration of the mental and emotional field has impacted the protoplasmic substance of our cells which, like the iron filings, are shaped by the magnetic properties of thoughts and emotions. Remember, despite dense appearances, the protoplasmic substances of our body are energy.

Emotion is the feminine aspect of creation, (will) magnetism. Thought is the masculine aspect of creation, electrical. Consciousness and beliefs are the manifesting presence that give form to the disease. Disease occurs when the process for the manifestation of form is complete. It begins first in the spiritual Body, then steps down into the physical body.

Designer Diseases

We live, have multiple experiences, and we judge those experiences. We have a particular way-of-being in the world and a way of responding to people and situations. The judgements are attached to a feeling state, love or fear, which in turn brings forth an emotion, e.g., anger, resentment, etc. We each judge situations differently and therefore miscreate differently. Think about how differently siblings growing up in the same family describe, interpret, and judge the events of that family life. Therefore, our dis-eases are designer creations designed around our experiences and how we have judged them. We are the designer. Disease is our unique creation. The emotion that is attached to the judgement is a factor in creating our designer disease. Depending upon the emotion, judgement, and thought we manifest different diseases.

Where disease finally manifests in the body is a function of the Chakra most impacted by the emotion's disharmony, and whether it is a past or present situation, masculine and/or feminine relational issues, genetic material, and our spiritual reason for incarnating at this time. Which organ is affected is a function of the symbolic Body/mind relationship or the metaphysical functionof that organ. The guidelines for discerning this information are covered in the basic information about each of the eleven Chakras in Chapter Two.

Inner and Outer Pollution

We are our environment. There is no separation . What affects the Earth affects us, and what affects us affects the earth. We are all within the circle of this vibrational network. Our electro-magnetic energy system/Body vibrates in synchrony with the energy fields of the earth. We have a bioresonance entrainment with the earth's electromagnetic, gravitational, and energetic fields. If we didn't, we would not be able to stay here on earth; the dissonance would destroy our energy field. In our arrogance we cling to the illusion that we are separate from the earth, air, water, plant life, and from our relatives that are four legged, winged, etc. Our inner polluted consciousness has created the outer pollution of global warming, holes in the ozone layer, etc. Burning SUVs' on auto dealers' lots does not change the consciousness that created engines that create toxic exhaust. Working to improve our health and our consciousness is a step in the right direction, but it's important to understand that we cannot achieve optimal health until we weave a tapestry of health for the planet.

Our separation from our higher selves and our Creator, as well as our arrogance has disconnected us from our spiritual roots. We mirror that consciousness and disconnect by creating a technology that produces substances that interfere with the sacred act of conservation and distribution of vital energy to and in the Body. These substances are environmental pollutants, including petroleum derivatives, heavy metals (mercury, aluminum, lead, arsenic, radium, and fluoride), and radiation. Radiation includes nuclear radiation, x-rays, as well as electromagnetic radiation from electrical power, computers, microwaves, cordless and cell phones. Petroleum derivatives can result in allergies, hair loss, fluid retention, and problems with calcium absorption as well as greater susceptibility to viral infections. Heavy metals are linked to neurological disorders. For example, there is a possible linkage of aluminum to Alzheimer's disease and Parkinson's disease (Gerber, pg 452). It is also suggested that mercury may be responsible for a considerable amount of undiagnosed chronic illness(Gerber, pg 453). Radiation has been linked to cancer, premature aging, lupus, and fetal abnormalities. Microwaves are linked to the development of cataracts (Gerber, pgs 456 &459).

Conventional safety limits in regards to environmental pollutants do not take into consideration the vibrational effects of these pollutants. Specifically, the discordant energy that they carry interferes with the balanced vibrational relationship of our Body's energy system. These substances interfere with the integrative, self regulating, communicative functions of the Body's energy system.

Changes in our consciousness are necessary. We can kindle the energy of love and cultivate a caretaker mind so that our thoughts give birth to a creative means of transforming technology in ways that support a tapestry of health for the planet

Chapter Three Summary

1. Our thoughts, words, and emotions are manifested in the physical body by our consciousness.
2. When the lower mind or material consciousness dominates we are in separation from our Creator.
3. Illness is a messenger carrying information about an imbalance or block in energy flow.
4. There are four things to consider when decoding the message: front side or backside, left or right side, which Chakra, and what is the time lapse between the upset and the symptom.
5. An upset results when a judgement is made about an event.; Upset= Event+Judgement.
6. To end the cycle of miscreation we acknowledge and take responsibility for our miscreations,
we forgive ourselves, we look with love upon our miscreations but withdraw our belief in them.
7. Our diseases are designer creations uniquely created by our thoughts, emotions, judgements of our experiences and the metaphysical function of the organ system.
8. Disease begins first in the spiritual body, then manifests in the physical body.
9. We are our environment, our inner polluted consciousness has created our outer polluted environment

The West

The Western energy enables us to transmute
in the fire of the setting sun.
As darkness descends, we death the ego
merging fully with our spiritual
consciousness. We arise with the new day,
where we may carry forth in
harmony with the present.

Chapter Four
Eleven Day Journey

THE JOURNEY BEGINS
There will come a time in your life when all you can do
is love. You will have done all you can do, tried all you
can try, hurt all you can hurt, given up so many times
that love will be the only way in or out. That day will
surely come. Just as sure as you are reading this page.
In the meantime, here are a few things you can do to
get ready for the most joyous day of your life: the day
you experience true love.
Iyanla Vanzant, <u>In The Meantime</u>

Change destroys what went before. Change sweeps
away the under brush so that our consciousness can
receive the nourishing Sun light. The process you will use
in this chapter clears the underbrush. It is your process,
your work. It offers an opportunity to clear the emotional
underbrush, extract the thorns of pain, and cut the weeds
of judgements that choke new growth. We will start by
clearing and healing the in body Chakras beginning with
the first Chakra, then proceed to the seventh Chakra,
alternating upper and lower Chakras. I do it this way to
avoid a pressure cooker effect where the lower Chakras
are open and energy is flowing but the upper ones are
blocked. Once we have cleared the in-body Chakras, we
will clear the out of body Chakras.

This journey, as with any journey, begins with setting
a date. So right now get out your calender and mark off
eleven days for your journey. Set your start date and your
end date. Now set a time. You want to devote one half
hour twice a day to your journey. What times within the
24 hour day will you spend on the process outlined in this

chapter? Pick times that are realistic, supportive, and to which you can commit. Look around your home. Where is there a space that affords you quiet, solitude and privacy. If you do not have that space in your home, find some other place you can use or create such a space in your home. Obtain a journal. It can be a spiral notebook, a loose leaf notebook or a bound journal. I prefer the grade school black and white bound composition books. Consider purchasing a timer or decide how you will time your two half hour sessions, which will be divided into two five minute meditations and a twenty minute clearing session. During the time you are processing to clear and heal your Chakras, you may want to go back to chapter three and refamiliarize yourself with the judgements, emotions, thoughts, etc of the Chakra you are processing. You can also write down the judgements, emotions, thoughts, etc of the Chakra you are processing so that you recognize them when they come up during your day and record them in your journal so that they are available for your releasing session.

When all these items have been addressed, make a commitment. Write this in your journal!

I, *fill in your name)* _____ commit to devoting one half hour twice a day beginning on (*fill in the date)* ___ and ending it on (*fill in the date)* ___ to clearing and healing my Chakras.

On the actual day that you start your journey write the statement shown below in your journey journal:

Today (write actual date) I cease believing that I am my physical body only. I view my Body as it truly is -an energy system- and my physical body as an out picturing of my former thoughts and emotions. I confess that I surrendered my God-given power to create with my consciousness to my body. I believed in my miscreations, thus causing a separation in consciousness blocking energy from my life Source. I believed in the possibility of

96

upset and dis-ease, and in doing so I have limited my
Perfect Health. No more! This day I claim my divine
inheritance of perfect health. I acknowledge my oneness
with my Creator, my Source and my life Energy supply.

Sign your name

Approach processing with this book with an attitude of
openness and play. Be gentle with yourself as you release
and experiment with changes.

Day One   First Chakra

Sit comfortably in a chair or on the floor. If you are sitting
in a chair do not cross your legs or your arms so that the
energy can flow freely. Read over the instructions before
you start.

Five minute visualization: Visualize a spiral of energy
from your tail bone/ coccyx spiraling downwards through
the floor to the earth. Experience a return flow of energy
spiraling back to you. Breathe deeply through any images,
thoughts, emotions, or physical sensations you experience
during the visualization.

Twenty minute release and replacement. You are now
going to release judgements, thoughts, emotions,
behaviors and physical manifestations of blocked first
Chakra energy. Follow the chart below reading the
statement and the ***bolded italicized*** words out loud. Even
if you believe you are not experiencing these issues,
RELEASE. Some one on the planet is. Do it for them.
I release from my spiritual, mental, emotional,
and physical Body:

I'm Wrong, I'm right, They're wrong
Obstruction
Anger
Perfectionism, getting stuck; avoidance, delays, regret

and isolation
Circulatory problems, rectal problems, urinary tract
problems, chemical imbalances, dental problems, boils,
burns and infections.

Take five deep breaths. Inhale through your nose and exhale slowly through your nose, five times. If your nose is stopped up, then you may breathe through your mouth. You may experience some lightheadedness, tingling or yawning. These are signs of energy flowing.

Make the sound LAM (begins with an open mouth with L, comes to the center of the mouth with A as in India, and ends with lips closed in M)

Visualize the healing colors white and pink in the area of the first Chakra front and back side.

Utilize the healing breath cycle 1/4 second: 1/8 second on the inhale and 1/8 second on the exhale. This is the bellows breath, a short inhale with the emphasis on the exhale using the abdominal muscles contraction to force the exhale.

Speak the statement out loud and say the *bolded italicized words* out loud.

I take into my spiritual, mental, emotional, and physical Body: *I surrender; I'm happy in my unlimited abundance.*

Five minute meditation: Sit quietly with your eyes closed breathing normally. Slowly bring your awareness back to your surroundings and open your eyes.

Observation During the Day

During your day pay attention to any judgements, thoughts, emotions, behaviors and physical manifestations related to the first Chakra blockage. Don't get caught up in them. Just note that they are coming up. Breath your five count breath when they do and speak your God conscious decision.

I surrender.

Sit comfortably in a chair or on the floor to begin your second half hour session. Remember not to cross your legs or arms.

Five minute visualization: Visualize a spiral of energy from your tail bone/ coccyx spiraling downwards through the floor to the earth. Experience a return flow of energy spiraling back to you. Breath deeply through any images, thoughts, emotions, or physical sensations you experience during the visualization.

Twenty minute release and replacement: Write down in your journal, using one or two word cues, any experiences you had during the day in which blocked first Chakra judgements, thoughts, emotions, behaviors or physical manifestations were experienced. For example if you were in a meeting and experienced that you were wrong or being told you are wrong, that is the judgement "I'm wrong" or if you experienced "I'm right." Just write the cue word "meeting." Your subconscious has recorded the entire incident. It's on your subconscious tape. The cue word will bring forth the tape. You don't need to duplicate another tape of it by writing out all the details. Allow the one or two word association with the experience to come forward. It may be the name of a person, a color, a place, etc. Don't get caught up with trying to grammatically word craft the two word associations to the statement. Initially, the associations may come slowly but gradually they will come faster. Take 3 minutes to write out word association cues for all the times during the day you experienced any judgement, thought, emotion, behavior and/or physical manifestation associated with a blocked first Chakra. Read each association one at a time. Repeat the statement below, filling each cue word into the blank space one at a time, as you read the statement. You will repeat the statement each time you fill in a different word cue. If you don't remember, or don't recognize that anything came up that's fine, just go back to page 97 and fill the **bolded italicized** words on the chart one at a time into the blank space of the statement below. Begin now.

This ....has no meaning to me. I release and rise above that upset to a time and a place where it has no power over me.

Each time after reading the statement, take five deep breaths. Inhale through your nose and exhale slowly through your nose five times. If your nose is stopped up, then you may breathe through your mouth. You may experience some lightheadedness, tingling or yawning. These are signs of energy flowing. Read the next word cue filling in the blank of the statement. Then take your breath. Repeat this process for the remainder of the twenty minutes or until you have released all the word cues you wrote down, whichever comes first. If you had no word cues and are using the chart from page 97 keep repeating the words until the twenty minutes are up. When you are finished, repeat your God Conscious decision:

I surrender; I'm happy in my unlimited abundance.
Five minute meditation: Sit quietly with your eyes closed breathing normally. Slowly bring your awareness back to your surroundings and open your eyes. Congratulations! You have now completed your first day's journey.

Day Two Seventh Chakra

Sit comfortably in a chair or on the floor. If you are sitting in a chair keep you legs and arms uncrossed. Please read the instructions before you begin.
Five minute visualization: Visualize a spiral of energy inside your skull spiraling upwards out of the "soft spot" at the center of your head. Experience a return flow of

energy spiraling back to you. The flows merge into a continuous stream of energy like a cap enveloping your head.

Breathe deeply through any images, thoughts, emotions, or physical sensations you experience during the visualization.

 Twenty minute release and replacement. You are now going to release judgements, thoughts, emotions, behaviors and physical manifestations of blocked seventh Chakra energy. Follow the chart below reading statement out loud and the ***bolded italicized*** words out loud. Even if you believe you are not experiencing these issues RELEASE. Some one on the planet is. Do it for them.

I release from my spiritual, mental, emotional, and physical Body:

Life's a Struggle, God Doesn't Support Me
Overload.
No Sympathy
Workaholic, overwhelmed, it's too much, I can't handle it
High blood pressure, learning disabilities, mental illness and ***alcoholism***

Take five deep breaths. Inhale through your nose and exhale slowly through your nose five times. If your nose is stopped up, then you may breathe through your mouth. You may experience some lightheadedness, tingling or yawning. These are signs of energy flowing.

Make the Sound- MMM (made with the lips together so the sound is within the hollow of the mouth)

Visualize the healing colors golden yellow and violet in the area of the cap of energy flow at the crown of your head.

 Utilize the healing sixteen seconds breath cycle: eight on the inhale and eight on the exhale.

Speak the statement out loud and say the bolded italicized word out loud.

I take into my spiritual, mental, emotional, and physical Body:

I Am expressing in all aspects of my life my vision of divine purpose; God supports me.

Five minute meditation: Sit quietly with your eyes closed breathing normally. Slowly bring your awareness back to your surroundings and open your eyes.

Observation During the Day

During your day pay attention to any judgements, thoughts, emotions, behaviors and physical manifestations related to the seventh Chakra blockage. Don't get caught up in them. Just note that they are coming up. Breathe your five count breath when they do and speak your God conscious decision.

God Supports Me.

Sit comfortably in a chair or on the floor to begin your second half hour session.

Five minute visualization: Visualize a spiral of energy inside your skull spiraling upwrds out the "soft spot" at the center of your head. Experience a return flow of energy spiraling back to you. The flows merge into one continuous stream of golden yellow and violet energy like a cap enveloping your head. Breathe deeply through any images, thoughts, emotions, or physical sensations you experience during the visualization.

Twenty minute release and replacement: Write down in your journal, using one or two word cues, any experiences you had during the day in which blocked seventh Chakra judgements, thoughts, emotions, behaviors or physical manifestations were experienced. For example, note if you were talking to a friend and experienced overwhelm during the conversation. Just write the cue word of your friend's name. Your subconscious has recorded the entire incident. It's on your subconscious tape. The cue word will bring forth the tape. You don't need to duplicate another tape of it by recalling the details of the entire event. Allow the one or two word cue associated with the experience to come forward. It may be the name of a place, a smell, etc. Initially, the word associations may come slowly but gradually they will come faster. Take 3 minutes and write out one or two words cues for the situations in That you experienced any judgements, thoughts, emotions, behaviors and or physical manifestations of seventh Chakra blocks during the day. Repeat the statement below, filling each association word cue into the blank space, one at a time, as you read the statement. You will be repeating the entire statement each time you fill in a different word cue. If you have no remembered experiences, use the bolded words from the chart on page 101.

This ....has no meaning to me. I release and rise above that upset to a time and a place where it has no power over me.

Take five deep breaths. Inhale through your nose and exhale slowly through your nose five times. If your nose is stopped up, then you may breath through your mouth. You may experience some lightheadedness, tingling or yawning. These are signs of energy flowing. Read the next word cue filling the cues into the blank space. Then take your breath. Repeat this process for the remainder of the twenty minutes or until you have released all the word cues, whichever comes first. If you are using the words on the chart, keep repeating them until the twenty minutes are up. When you are finished, repeat your God Conscious decision:

I Am expressing in all aspects of my life, my vision of divine purpose; God supports me.

Five minute meditation: Sit quietly with your eyes closed breathing normally. Slowly bring your awareness back to your surroundings and open your eyes. Congratulations! You have now completed your second day of your journey.

Day Three Second Chakra

Sit comfortably in a chair or on the floor. If you are sitting in a chair do not cross your legs or your arms. Review the instructions before beginning.

Five minute visualization: Visualize a spiral of energy from your genital area spiraling out the front of the body. Visualize it spiraling out to an arms length from the body. Now visualize a spiral of energy spiraling out an arm's length from the back of the body just above the parting of the buttocks. Visualize a return flow of sunlight spiraling back to your front side to your genitals, and back side, to the back of the body just above the parting of the buttocks.. Experience your Body absorbing that energy until there is no distinct spiral stream. Breathe deeply through any images, thoughts, emotions, or physical sensations you experience during the visualization.

Twenty minute release and replacement. You are now going to release judgements, thoughts, emotions, behaviors and physical manifestations of blocked second Chakra energy. Follow the chart below reading statement outloud and the **bolded italicized** words out loud. Even if you believe you are not experiencing these issues RELEASE. Some one on the planet is. Do it for them. We are all related.

I release from my spiritual, mental, emotional, and physical Body:
Aliveness Hurts or Kills
Hostile
Hostility

Wanting to kill, murderous actions, criticism, gossip and pushy aggressiveness
Infections of all types, arthritis, stress, lower back pain, allergies, migraines, accident proneness, disease in the reproductive system, sexual dysfunction, sexual manipulation, sterility, and sexual abuse

Take five deep breaths, Inhale through your nose and exhale slowly through your nose five times. If your nose is stopped up, then you may breath through your mouth. You may experience some lightheadedness, tingling or yawning. These are signs of energy flowing.

Make the sound VAM (V at the back of an open mouth, A as in father and M with the lips closed)

Visualize the healing colors : Pastel peach and violet in the area of the second Chakra front and back side..

Utilize the healing ½ second breath cycle: an inhale and an exhale within the span of ½ second. It is similar to a panting breath or the bellows breath used in the first Chakra exercise but slower.

Speak the statement out loud and say the *bolded italicized words* out loud.

I take into my spiritual, mental, emotional, and physical Body:

My aliveness heals; My pleasure pleases God .

Five minute meditation: Sit quietly with your eyes closed breathing normally. Slowly bring your awareness back to your surroundings and open your eyes.

Observation During the Day

During your day pay attention to any judgements, thoughts, emotions, behaviors and physical manifestations related to the second Chakra blockage. Don't get caught up in them. Just note that they are coming up. Breathe your five count breath when they do and speak your God conscious decision.

My pleasure pleases God.

Sit comfortably in a chair or on the floor to begin your second half hour session. Remember not to cross your legs or arms.

Five minute visualization: Visualize a spiral of energy from your genital area spiraling out to an arms length from the front of the body. Now visualize a spiral of energy spiraling out from the lower back just above the parting of the buttocks. Visualize that energy spiraling out to an arm's length from the body. Visualize a return flow of pastel peach and violet energy spiraling back to the front and backside of your second Chakra. Experience you Body absorbing that energy until there is no distinct spiral stream. Breathe deeply through any images, thoughts, emotions, or physical sensations you experience during the visualization.

Twenty minute release and replacement: Write down in your journal using one or two word cues, any experiences you had during the day in which blocked second Chakra judgements, thoughts, emotions, behaviors or physical manifestations were experienced. For example, note if you were at lunch and gossiping about someone. That is behavior blocking the second Chakra. Just write the cue word "gossip." Your subconscious has recorded the entire incident. It's on your subconscious tape. The cue word will bring forth the experience. Allow the one or two words associated with the experience to come forward. It may be the name of a person, a sound, a place, etc. Don't get caught up with trying to grammatically word craft the associations to the statement. Take 3 minutes now and write out word association cues for all the times during the day you experienced any judgement, thought, emotion, behavior and/or physical manifestation associated with a blocked second Chakra. Reading each associations one at a time, repeat the statement below and fill the cue word into the

106

blank space. If you don't remember, or don't recognize that anything came up, that's fine. Just go back to page 104 and 105 fill the **bolded italicized** words on the chart one at a time into the blank space of the statement below. You may begin.

This ....has no meaning to me I release and rise above that upset to a time and a place where it has no power over me.

Each time after reading the statement, take five deep breaths. Inhale through your nose and exhale slowly through your nose five times. If your nose is stopped up, then you may breathe through your mouth. You may experience some lightheadedness, tingling or yawning. These are signs of energy flowing. Read the next word cue filing in the blank of the statement. Then take your breath. Repeat this process for the remainder of the twenty minutes or until you have released all the word cues you wrote down, whichever comes first. If you had no word cues and are using the chart from page 104 and 105, keep repeating the words on the chart until the twenty minutes are up. When you are finished repeat your God Conscious decision:

My aliveness heals; My pleasure pleases God.

Five minute meditation: Sit quietly with your eyes closed breathing normally. Slowly bring your awareness back to your surroundings and open your eyes. Congratulations! You have now completed three day's of your journey.

Day Four Sixth Chakra

Sit comfortably in a chair or on the floor. Read the instructions before beginning.

Five minute visualization: Visualize a spiral of energy beginning inside your skull and coming out the space between your eyebrows. The energy extends out an arm's length from your body. Now visualize a spiral of energy beginning in your skull and coming out the back of your head. This energy also extends out an arm's length from the back of your head. Visualize an energy spiral of rose-pink and purplish -blue like a a halo around your eyebrows, ears and the back of the head. Allow the halo to slowly dissolve and become absorbed within your skull. Breathe deeply through any images, thoughts, emotions, or physical sensations you experience during the visualization.

Twenty minute release and replacement. You are now going to release judgements, thoughts, emotions, behaviors and physical manifestations of blocked sixth Chakra energy. Follow the chart below reading the **_bolded italicized_** words out loud after the statement. Even if you believe you are not experiencing these issues RELEASE. Some one on the planet is. Do it for them.

I release from my spiritual, mental, emotional, and physical Body:

Confusion, I'm Opposite
Irritation
Antagonism
People, situations, events that get on my nerves, keeping people at a distance, and **_being misunderstood_**
Endocrine imbalances, skin irritation, sinusitis, shingles, eyesight problems, headaches

Take five deep breaths. Inhale through your nose and exhale slowly through your nose five times. If your nose is stopped up then you may breath through your mouth. You may experience some lightheadedness, tingling or yawning. these are signs of energy flowing.

Make the sound OM (begins with an open mouth with O and end with lips closed in M)

Visualize the healing colors deep purple and emerald green in the area of the sixth Chakra front and back.

Utilize the 8 seconds healing breath cycle: 4 seconds on the inhale and 4 seconds on the exhale.

experiences you had during the day in which blocked sixth Chakra judgements, thoughts, emotions, behaviors or physical manifestations were experienced. For example, note if you thought that someone was irritating or felt antagonistic towards some one. Just write the persons name. Your subconscious has recorded the entire incident. The person's name will bring forth the tape. Allow the one or two word association with the experience to come forward. It may be a sound, an article of clothing, etc. Don't get caught up with trying to grammatically word craft the word associations to the statement. Take 3 minutes and write out word association cues for all the times during the day you experienced any judgement, thought, emotion, behavior and/or physical manifestation associated with a blocked sixth Chakra. Read each associations one at a time, repeating the statement and filling the cue word into the blank space. If you don't recognize that anything came up, that's fine. Just go back to page 108 and fill the *bolded italicized* words on the chart one at a time into the blank space of the statement below.

This ....has no meaning to me I release and rise above that upset to a time and a place where it has no power over me.

Each time after reading the statement, take five deep breaths. Inhale through your nose and exhale slowly through your nose five times. If your nose is stopped up, then you may breathe through your mouth. You may experience some lightheadedness, tingling or yawning. These are signs of energy flowing. Read the next word cue filing in the blank of the statement. Then take your breath. Repeat this process for the remainder of the twenty minutes or until you have released all the word cues you wrote down, whichever comes first. If you had no word cues and are using the chart from page 108, keep repeating the words on the chart until the twenty minutes are up. When you are finished repeat your God Conscious decision:

I'm certain of my path and purpose; God's creation pleasures me

Five minute meditation: Sit quietly with your eyes closed breathing normally. Slowly bring your awareness back to your surroundings and open your eyes. Congratulations! Your fourth day's journey is complete.

Day Five Third Chakra

Sit comfortably in a chair or on the floor. Remember to keep your arms and legs uncrossed.

Five minute meditation: Visualize a spiral of energy beginning at your spine opposite your navel area coming forward and out your abdominal area above and below the belly button. Visualize it spiraling out to an arm's length in front of your body. Visualize another spiral originating in the same area of your spine but spiraling out your lower middle back extending out an arms length from your back. Experience energy returning to the abdominal and back area. Visualize the abdominal and back areas bathed in orange and green. Watch these colors become absorbed into your back and abdomen.

Twenty minute release and replacement. You are now going to release judgements, thoughts, emotions, behaviors and physical manifestations of blocked third Chakra energy. Follow the chart below reading the statement and the *bolded italicized* words out loud. Even if you believe you are not experiencing these issues RELEASE anyway. Some one on the planet is experiencing these issues. Do it for them.

I release from my spiritual, mental, emotional, and physical Body:

Unworthy to receive

Loss

Hate

Scarcity, experiencing myself as lacking love, money, sexual fulfillment, power ;having difficulty receiving from others, hiding my gifts, my skills, my talents; loss of love, friends, divorce, property

Loss of organs or limbs, loss of body, aging, abdominal organ problems

Take five deep breaths.Inhale through your nose and exhale slowly through your nose five times. If your nose is stopped up, then you may breathe through your mouth. You may experience some lightheadedness, tingling or yawning. These are signs of energy flowing.

Make the sound RAM (begins with an open mouth with R comes to the center of the mouth with A as in India, and ends with lips closed in M)

Visualize the healing colors gold and ruby in the area of the third Chakra front and backside.

Utilize the one second healing breath cycle: ½ second on the inhale and ½ second on the exhale.

Speak the statement below out loud and say the **bolded italicized words** out loud

I take into my spiritual, mental, emotional, and physical Body:

I joyfully express my God-given ideas; God loves through me.

Five minute meditation: Sit quietly with your eyes closed breathing normally. Slowly bring your awareness back to your surroundings and open your eyes.

Observation During the Day

During your day pay attention to any judgements, thoughts, emotions, behaviors and physical manifestations related to the Third Chakra blockage. Don't get caught up in them. Just note that they are coming up. Breathe your five count breath when they do and speak your God conscious decision.

God loves through me.

Sit comfortably in a chair or on the floor to begin your second half hour session. Remember do not to cross your legs or arms.

Five minute visualization: Visualize a spiral of energy beginning at your spine opposite your navel area coming forward and out your abdominal area above and below the belly button. Visualize it spiraling out to an arm's length in front of your body. Visualize another spiral originating in the same area of your spine but spiraling out your lower middle back extending out an arms length from your back. Experience energy returning to the abdominal and back area. Visualize these areas bathed in gold and ruby. Watch these colors become absorbed into your back and abdomen.

 Twenty minute release and replacement: Write down in your journal, using one or two word cues, any experiences you had during the day in which blocked third Chakra judgements, thoughts, emotions, behaviors or physical manifestations were experienced. For example, note if someone told you about a mutual friend getting a divorce, or someone expressed hatred in your presence. Just write the cue word. Your subconscious has recorded the entire incident. It's on your subconscious tape. The cue word will bring forth the tape. Allow the one or two word association with the experience to come forward. It may be the name of a person, a color, a place, etc. Don't get caught up with trying to grammatically word craft the word associations to the statement. Now, take 3 minutes and write out word association cues for all the times during the day you experienced personally or in relation to someone else, any judgement, thought, emotion, behavior and/or physical manifestation associated with a blocked third Chakra. Reading each associations one at a time, repeat the statement and fill the cue word into the blank space. If you don't remember, or don't recognize that anything came up, that's fine. Just go back to page 110 and 111 and fill the **bolded italicized** words on the chart one at a time into the blank space of the statement below. Begin now.

This ....has no meaning to me. I release and rise above that upset to a time and a place where it has no power over me.

Each time after reading the statement, take five deep breaths. Inhale through your nose and exhale slowly through your nose five times. If your nose is stopped up, then you may breath through your mouth. You may experience some lightheadedness, tingling or yawning. These are signs of energy flowing. Read the next word cue filling in the blank of the statement. Then take your breath. Repeat this process for the remainder of the twenty minutes or until you have released all the word cues you wrote down, whichever comes first. If you had no word cues and are using the chart from page 110 and 111, keep repeating the words on the chart until the twenty minutes are up. When you are finished repeat your God Conscious decision:

I joyfully express my God-given ideas; God loves through me.

Five minute meditation: Sit quietly with your eyes closed breathing normally. Slowly bring your awareness back to your surroundings and open your eyes. Congratulations, you have completed five days of your journey.

Day Six Fifth Chakra

Sit comfortably in a chair or on the floor.

Five minute meditation: Visualize a spiral of silvery blue energy beginning at the hollow of your throat and moving around your neck like a turtleneck collar. Watch this color become absorbed into your throat and the back of your neck.

Twenty minute release and replacement. You are now going to release judgements, thoughts, emotions, behaviors and physical manifestations of blocked fifth Chakra energy. Follow the chart below reading the statement outloud and the ***bolded italicized*** words out loud. Even if you believe you are not experiencing these issues, RELEASE anyway. Some one on the planet is experiencing these issues. Do it for them.

I release from my spiritual, mental, emotional, and physical Body:

I'm Unlovable, Unworthy of God's Love
Rejection
Pain, guilt, blame, grief, anxiety
Victimization, being misunderstood, not being heard, feeling unlovable, abdication of responsibility.
Throat infections, thyroid problems, ear aches

Take five deep breathes. Inhale through your nose and exhale slowly through your nose five times. If your nose is stopped up, then you may breathe through your mouth. You may experience some lightheadedness, tingling or yawning. These are signs of energy flowing.

Make the sound HAM

Visualize the healing colors cobalt blue in the area of the fifth Chakra front and backside.

Utilize the 4 seconds healing breath cycle: 2 seconds on the inhale and 2 second on the exhale.

Speak the statement below out loud and say the *bolded italicized words* out loud

I take into my spiritual, mental, emotional, and physical Body:

I 'm Creative; God Accepts me

Five minute meditation: Sit quietly with your eyes closed breathing normally. Slowly bring your awareness back to your surroundings and open your eyes.

Observation During the Day

During your day pay attention to any judgements, thoughts, emotions, behaviors and physical manifestations related to the fifth Chakra blockage. Don't get caught up in them. Just note that they are coming up. Breathe your five count breath when they do and speak your God conscious decision.

God Accepts me

Sit comfortably in a chair or on the floor to begin your second half hour session.

Five minute meditation: Visualize a spiral of silvery blue energy beginning at the hollow of your throat and moving around your neck like a turtleneck collar. Watch this color become absorbed into your throat and the back of your neck.

Twenty minute release and replacement: Write down in your journal using one or two word cues, any experiences you had during the day in which blocked sixth Chakra judgements, thoughts, emotions, behaviors or physical manifestations were experienced. For example, note if you experienced emotional pain, or thought you were misunderstood. Just write a cue word. Your subconscious has recorded the entire incident. It's on your subconscious tape. The cue word will bring forth the tape. Allow the one or two word association with the experience to come forward. It may be the name of a situation, a person, etc. Don't get caught up with trying to grammatically word craft the cue word associations to the statement. Take 3 minutes and write out word association cues for all the times during the day you experienced personally or in relation to someone else, any judgement, thought, emotion, behavior and/or physical manifestation associated with a blocked fifth Chakra. Read each association one at a time, repeating the statement and filling the cue word into the blank space. You will repeat the entire statement each time you fill in a different word cue. If you don't remember, or don't recognize that anything came up, that's fine. Just go back to page 114, and fill the **bolded italicized** words on the chart one at a time into the blank space of the statement below. Begin now.

This ....has no meaning to me. I release and rise above that upset to a time and a place where it has no power over me.

Each time after reading the statement, take five deep breaths. Inhale through your nose and exhale slowly through your nose five times. If your nose is stopped up, then you may breath through your mouth. You may experience some light headedness, tingling or yawning.These are signs of energy flowing. Read the next word cue filling in the blank of the statement. Then take your breath. Repeat this process for the remainder of the twenty minutes or until you have released all the word cues you wrote down, whichever comes first. If you had no word cues and are using the chart from page 114, keep repeating the words on the chart until the twenty minutes are up. When you are finished repeat your God Conscious decision:

I'm Creative; God Accepts me

Five minute meditation: Sit quietly with your eyes closed breathing normally. Slowly bring your awareness back to your surroundings and open your eyes. Congratulations you have completed half of your journey.

Day Seven Fourth Chakra

Sit comfortably in a chair or on the floor.

Five minute meditation: Visualize a spiral of golden light coming from your chest between your breast. Now, visualize golden light coming from your upper back where the shoulder blades begin. Visualize the light extending outwards from your body the distance of one arm's length on the frontside, then visualize the same on the backside. Visialize it, like a beam of light from a flashlight, getting larger the further it distances from your body. Breath deeply through your heart area, experiencing energy flowing through your chest. Continue to breathe in the heart area through any images, thoughts, emotions, or physical sensations you experience.

Twenty minute release and replacement. You are now going to release judgements, thoughts, emotions, behaviors and physical manifestations of blocked fourth Chakra energy. Follow the chart below reading the statement out loud and the ***bolded italicized*** words out loud. Even if you believe you are not experiencing these issues RELEASE anyway. Some one on the planet is experiencing these issues. Do it for them. We are all related.

I release from my spiritual, mental, emotional, and physical Body:

I'm not enough, I'm too much
Sterility
Resentment, self abasement, terror
Unproductive, being prolific, temperamental, lacking authority
Heart trouble, coughing, lung problems, stiff neck

Take five deep breaths. Inhale through your nose and exhale slowly through your nose five times. If your nose is stopped up, then you may breathe through your mouth. You may experience some lightheadedness, tingling or yawning. These are signs of energy flowing.

Make the sound YAM

Visualize the healing colors pink in the area of the fourth Chakra front and backside.

Utilize the 2 seconds healing breath cycle: 1 second on the inhale and 1 second on the exhale.

Speak the statement below out loud and say the **bolded it** *lalicized words* out *loud.*

I take into my spiritual, mental, emotional, and physical Body:

 I am Love in balance; The universe is perfect.

Five minute meditation: Sit quietly with your eyes closed breathing normally. Slowly bring your awareness back to your surroundings and open your eyes.

Observation During the Day

During your day pay attention to any judgements, thoughts, emotions, behaviors and physical manifestations related to the fourth Chakra blockage. Don't get caught up in them. Just note that they are coming up. Breathe your five count breath when they do and speak your God conscious decision.

The Universe is Perfect

Sit comfortably in a chair or on the floor to begin your second half hour session.

Five minute meditation: Visualize a spiral of golden light coming from your chest between your breast. Now visualize a spiral of golden light coming from your upper back where the shoulder blades begin. Visualize the light extending outwards to the front and back the distance of arm's length from your body, and like a flash light beam, getting larger the further it distances from your body.

Breathe deeply through your heart area experiencing the spiraling energy flowing through your chest. Continue to breathe through any images, thoughts, emotions, or physical sensations you experience.

Twenty minute release and replacement: Write down in your journal, using one or two word cues, any experiences you had during the day in which blocked fourth Chakra judgements, thoughts, emotions, behaviors or physical manifestations were experienced. For example, note if you experienced not being productive, or felt unloved or that your authority was being undermined. Just write a cue word. Your subconscious has recorded the entire incident. It's on your subconscious tape. The cue word will bring forth the tape. Allow the one or two word association with the experience to come forward. It may be the name of a person, situation, a color, etc. Don't get caught up with trying to grammatically word craft the cue word associations to the statement. Take 3 minutes and write out word association cues for all the times during the day you experienced personally or in relation to someone else, any judgement, thought, emotion, behavior and/or physical manifestation associated with a blocked fourth Chakra. Read each associations one at a time, repeat the statement, fill the cue word into the blank space one at a time as you read the statement. You will repeat the entire statement each time you fill in a different word cue. If you don't remember, or don't recognize that anything came up, that's fine. Just go back to page 117 and fill the **_bolded italicized_** words on the chart one at a time into the blank space of the statement below. Begin now.

This ....has no meaning to me. I release and rise above that upset to a time and a place where it has no power over me.

Each time after reading the statement take five deep breaths. Inhale through your nose and exhale slowly through your nose five times. If your nose is stopped up, then you may breath through your mouth. You may experience some light headedness, tingling or yawning. These are signs of energy flowing. Read the next word cue filling in the blank of the statement. Then take your breath. Repeat this process for the remainder of the twenty minutes or until you have released all the word cues you wrote down, whichever comes first. If you had no word cues and are using the chart from page 117, keep repeating the words on the chart until the twenty minutes are up. When you are finished repeat your God Conscious decision:

I am love in balance; The Universe is perfect.
Five minute meditation: Sit quietly with your eyes closed breathing normally. Slowly bring your awareness back to your surroundings and open your eyes. Congratulations you have completed seven days of your journey.

Day Eight Eighth Chakra
Sit comfortably in a chair or on the floor.
Five minute meditation: Visualize a plate like spiral of energy the color of mother of pearl 1 to1 and ½ inches above the crown Chakra. The spiral may change shape as you do your visualization. Don't attempt to hold it to any particular form.
Twenty minute release and replacement. You are now going to release judgements, thoughts, emotions, behaviors and physical manifestations of blocked eighth Chakra energy. Follow the chart below reading the *bolded italicized* words out loud after the statement. Even if you believe you are not experiencing these issues RELEASE anyway. Some one on the planet is experiencing these issues. Do it for them.

I release from my spiritual, mental, emotional, and physical Body:

I'm Stuck in the Past
I'm independent of everything and everybody
Fear, apprehension;
Opposition, fighting other peoples or authority figures influence or control
Recurring physical, emotional and relationship problems

Take five deep breaths. Inhale through your nose and exhale slowly through your nose five times. If your nose is stopped up, then you may breath through your mouth. You may experience some lightheadedness, tingling or yawning. These are signs of energy flowing.

Make the sound HAM

Visualize the a healing white and gold light in the area of the eighth Chakra 1 and ½ inches above your head.

Utilize the 24 seconds healing breath cycle: 12 seconds on the inhale and 12 second on the exhale.

Speak the statement below out loud and say the ***bolded italicized words*** out loud

I take into my spiritual, mental, emotional, and physical Body:

I Am on purpose in this lifetime; I express my sacred purpose in a timely manner.

Five minute meditation: Sit quietly with your eyes closed breathing normally. Slowly bring your awareness back to your surroundings and open your eyes.

Observation During the Day

During your day pay attention to any judgements, thoughts, emotions, behaviors and physical manifestations related to the eighth Chakra blockage. Don't get caught up in them. Just note that they are coming up. Breath your five count breath when they do and speak your God conscious decision.

I Am on purpose in this lifetime

Sit comfortably in a chair or on the floor to begin your second half hour session.

Five minute meditation: Visualize a plate like spiral the color of mother of pearl energy 1 to 1 and ½ inches above the crown Chakra. Do not attempt to control the shape or form of the spiral.

Twenty minute release and replacement: Write down in your journal, using one or two word cues, any experiences you had during the day in which blocked eighth Chakra judgements, thoughts, emotions, behaviors or physical manifestations were experienced. For example, note if you experienced opposition to something that someone said or if you experienced fear. Just write a cue word. Your subconscious has recorded the entire incident. It's on your subconscious tape. The cue word will bring forth the tape. Allow the one or two word association with the experience to come forward. It may be a color, the name of a situation, etc. Don't get caught up with trying to grammatically word craft the cue word associations to the statement. Take 3 minutes and write out word association cues for all the times during the day you experienced personally or in relation to someone else, any judgement, thought, emotion, behavior and/or physical manifestation associated with a blocked eighth Chakra. Repeat the statement, filling each cue word into the blank space, one at a time, as you read the statement. You will repeat the entire statement each time you fill in a word cue. If you don't remember, or don't recognize that anything came up, that's fine. Just go back to page 121, and fill the **bolded italicized** words on the chart one at a time into the blank space of the statement below. Begin now.

This ....has no meaning to me. I release and rise above that upset to a time and a place where it has no power over me.

122

Each time after reading the statement, take five deep breaths. Inhale through your nose and exhale slowly through your nose five times. If your nose is stopped up, then you may breath through your mouth. You may experience some light headedness, tingling or yawning. These are signs of energy flowing. Read the next word cue filling in the blank of the statement. Then take your breathe. Repeat this process for the remainder of the twenty minutes or until you have released all the word cues you wrote down, whichever comes first. If you had no word cues and are using the chart from page 121, keep repeating the words on the chart until the twenty minutes are up. When you are finished repeat your God Conscious decision:

I Am on purpose in this lifetime; I express my sacred purpose in a timely manner.

Five minute meditation: Sit quietly with your eyes closed breathing normally. Slowly bring your awareness back to yoursurroundingss and open your eyes. Congratulationss you have completed day eight of your journey.

Day Nine Ninth Chakra
Sitcomfortablyy in a chair or on the floor.
Five minute meditation: Visualize a funnel of golden light hovering one arms length above your head. Experience white light like lightening coming from the funnel striking the top of your head and cascading down your back and penetrating each of the Chakrass from the eighth through the first. Don't worry about focusing on each Chakra being penetrated. Just set an intention that they will be penetrated and it will happen. Breath deeply for twenty breathes imagining the breath flowing upward along the front of the body from your first Chakra through the golden funnel and down your back to your first

123

Chakra. It will become a continuous circular stream of white light. Continue to breathe until you have completed twenty breathes through any images, thoughts, emotions, or physical sensations you experience.

Twenty minute release andreplacement. You are now going to release judgements, thoughts, emotions, behaviors and physical manifestations of blocked ninth Chakra energy. Follow the chart below reading the *bolded italicized* words out loud after the statement. Even if you believe you are not experiencing these issues RELEASE anyway. Some one on the planet is experiencing these issues. Do it for them.

I release from my spiritual, mental, emotional, and physical Body:

Change hurts or Kills

Intolerance

Fear

Avoidance of examining beliefs, avoidance of feelings, avoidance of experiences that heighten my awareness, avoidance of insight, avoidance of healing, avoidance of change

All illness challenges from this life and all past lives.

Take five deep breaths. Inhale through your nose and exhale slowly through your nose. If your nose is stopped up, then you may breath through your mouth. You may experience some lightheadedness, tingling or yawning. These are signs of energy flowing.

Visualize the healing colors gold and white in the area of the ninth Chakra

Utilize the 24 seconds healing breath cycle: 12 seconds on the inhale and 12 seconds on the exhale.

Speak the statement below out loud and say the *bolded italicized words* out loud.

I take into my spiritual, mental, emotional, and physical Body:

"I am all that I have been, I am all that I would be, I am all that I Am (Byers) ; I have a true knowing of my gift and purpose at this time.

Five minute meditation: Sit quietly with your eyes closed breathing normally. Slowly bring your awareness back to your surroundings and open your eyes.

Observation During the Day

During your day pay attention to any judgements, thoughts, emotions, behaviors and physical manifestations related to the ninth Chakra blockage. Don't get caught up in them. Just note that they are coming up. Breath your five count breath when they do and speak your God conscious decision.

I Have a True Knowing of My Gift and Purpose at This Time

Sit comfortably in a chair or on the floor to begin your second half hour session.

Five minute meditation: Visualize a funnel of golden light hovering one arms length above your head. Experience white light like lightening coming from the funnel striking the top of your head and cascading down your back and penetrating each of the Chakras from the eighth through the first. Don't worry about attempting to control the light so it penetrates the Chakra. Just set the intention that it will. Breath deeply for twenty breathes imagining the breath flowing upward along the front of the body from your first Chakra through the golden funnel and down your back to your first Chakra until you are encircled front and back with white light.. Continue to breathe until you have completed twenty breathes through any images, thoughts, emotions, or physical sensations you experience.

Twenty minute release and replacement: Write down in your journal, using one or two word cues, any experiences you had during the day in which blocked ninth Chakra judgements, thoughts, emotions, behaviors or physical manifestations were experienced. For example, note if you experienced resistance to changing something or felt fear. Just write a cue word. Your subconscious has recorded the entire incident. It's on your subconscious tape. The cue word will bring forth the tape. Allow the one or two word association with the experience to come forward. It may be the name of a person, situation, a color, etc. Don't get caught up with trying to grammatically word craft the cue word associations to the statement. Take 3 minutes and write out word association cues for all the times during the day you experienced personally or in relation to someone else, any judgement, thought, emotion, behavior and/or physical manifestation associated with a blocked ninth Chakra. Read each association cue one at a time, filling each into the blank space, one at a time, as you repeat the statement. You will read the entire statement each time you fill in a different association cue. If you don't remember, or don't recognize that anything came up, that's fine. Just go back to page 124, and fill the **bolded italicized** words on the chart one at a time into the blank space of the statement below. Begin now.

This ....has no meaning to me. I release and rise above that upset to a time and a place where it has no power over me.

Each time after reading the statement, take five deep breaths. Inhale through your nose and exhale slowly through your nose five times. If your nose is stopped up, then you may breath through your mouth. You may experience some light headedness, tingling or yawning. These are signs of energy flowing. Read the next word cue filling in the blank of the statement.

Then take your breath. Repeat this process for the remainder of the twenty minutes or until you have released all the word cues you wrote down, whichever comes first. If you had no word cues and are using the chart from page 124, keep repeating the words on the chart until the twenty minutes are up. When you are finished repeat your God Conscious decision:
"I am all that I have been, I am all that I would be, I am all that I Am   (Byers) ; I have a true knowing of my gift and purpose at this time.
Five minute meditation: Sit quietly with your eyes closed breathing normally. Slowly bring your awareness back to your surroundings and open your eyes. Congratulations you have completed day nine of your journey.

Day Ten Tenth Chakra
Sit comfortably in a chair or on the floor. (Ideally this should be done outdoors standing on the ground)
Five minute meditation: Visualize a funnel of energy like a vacuum one half to four feet under your feet. Experience that this vacuum is sucking out wastes from your Body. As the waste leaves experience the centering of your purified Body. Visualize brown and green colors flowing up from below your feet moving up through your body to one arm's length above your head. Visualize it flowing back down your spine like obsidian lava, solidifying along your spine and back like a tree trunk with your legs and feet as roots anchored to the funnel four feet under your feet. Breath deeply for twenty breathes during your visualization. Continue to breathe until you have completed twenty breaths through any images, thoughts, emotions, or physical sensations you experience.
Twenty minute release and replacement. You are now going to release judgements, thoughts, emotions,

behaviors and physical manifestations of blocked ninth Chakra energy. Follow the chart below reading the **bolded italicized** words out loud after the statement. Even if you believe you are not experiencing these issues RELEASE anyway. Some one on the planet is experiencing these issues. Do it for them. We are all related.

I release from my spiritual, mental, emotional, and physical Body:

It's Painful to be Fully Here
Disconnected
Fear
Spaced-out, unfocused, accepting abuse, insecure, stressed out
Infections, hypertension, overweight, foot, ankle and leg problems

Take five deep breaths. Inhale through your nose and exhale slowly through your nose five times. If your nose is stopped up, then you may breath through your mouth. You may experience some lightheadedness, tingling or yawning. These are signs of energy flowing.

Visualize the healing colors pink and peach from the thighs down to the tenth Chakra four feet under your feet. Utilize the 16 seconds healing breath cycle : 8 seconds on the inhale and 8 seconds on the exhale.

Speak the statement below out loud and say the **bolded italicized words** out loud

I take into my spiritual, mental, emotional, and physical Body:

"I am fully here and able to cope; I am expressing my divine purpose in a grounded, practical way and enjoying life."

Five minute meditation: Sit quietly with your eyes closed breathing normally. Slowly bring your awareness back to your surroundings and open your eyes.

Observation During the Day

During your day pay attention to any judgements, thoughts, emotions, behaviors and physical manifestations related to the tenth Chakra blockage. Don't get caught up in them. Just note that they are coming up. Breathe your five count breath when they do and speak your God conscious decision.

"I am fully here and able to cope; I am expressing my divine purpose in a grounded, practical way and enjoying life."

Sit comfortably in a chair or on the floor to begin your second half hour session.

Five minute meditation: Visualize a funnel of energy like a vacuum one half to four feet under your feet. Visualize that this vacuum is sucking out wastes from your Body. As the waste leaves experience the centering of your purified Body. Visualize brown and green colors flowing up from below your feet to one arm's length above your head. Now visualiize it flowing back down your spine like obsidian lava, solidifying along your spine like a tree trunk with your legs and feet as roots anchored to the funnel four feet under your feet. Breath deeply for twenty breathes during your visualization. Continue to breathe until you have completed twenty breaths through any images, thoughts, emotions, or physical sensations you experience.

Twenty minute release and replacement: Write down in your journal, using one or two word cues, any experiences you had during the day in which blocked tenth Chakra judgements, thoughts, emotions, behaviors or physical manifestations were experienced. For example, note if you experienced a lack of focus, or stress, or disconnected. Just write a cue word. Your subconscious has recorded the entire incident. It's on your subconscious tape. The cue word will bring forth the tape.

Allow the one or two word association with the experience to come forward. It may be the name of a person, situation, a color, etc. Don't get caught up with trying to grammatically word craft the cue word associations to the statement. Take 3 minutes and write out word cues for all the times during the day you experienced personally or in relation to someone else, any judgement, thought, emotion, behavior and/or physical manifestation associated with a blocked ninth Chakra. Read each word cue, repeat the statement filling the word cue into the blank space, one at a time, as you read the statement. You will repeat the entire statement each time you fill in a different word cue. If you don't remember, or don't recognize that anything came up, that's fine. Just go back to page 128, and fill the *bolded italicized* words on the chart one at a time into the blank space of the statement below. Begin now.

This ....has no meaning to me I release and rise above that upset to a time and a place where it has no power over me.

Each time after reading the statement, take five deep breaths. Inhale through your nose and exhale slowly through your nose five times. If your nose is stopped up, then you may breathe through your mouth. You may experience some light headedness, tingling or yawning. These are signs of energy flowing. Read the next word cue filling in the blank of the statement. Then take your breath. Repeat this process for the remainder of the twenty minutes or until you have released all the word cues you wrote down, whichever comes first. If you had no word cues and are using the chart from page 128, keep repeating the words on the chart until the twenty minutes are up. When you are finished repeat your God Conscious decision:

"I am fully here, able to cope; I am expressing my divine purpose in a grounded, practical way and enjoying life."

Five minute meditation: Sit quietly with your eyes closed breathing normally. Slowly bring your awareness back to your surroundingss and open your eyes.

Congratulationss you have completed day ten of your journey.

Day Eleven Eleventh Chakra

Sit comfortably in a chair or on the floor remove your shoes and socks or stockings.

Five minute meditation: Visualize a spiral of pink energy in the palms of your hands and the soles of your feet. Bring the palms of your hands parallel to each other as if you are holding a ball six inches in diameter between your hands. Visualize and experience the energy passing back and fourth between your hands. Now bring your awareness to your feet. Stretch your legs out resting your feet on the heels so that the soles are not touching any surface. Visualize pink energy radiating from the soles of your feet. Breathe deeply for twenty breathes during your visualization. Continue to breathe until you have completed twenty breathes through any images, thoughts, emotions, or physical sensations you experience.

Twenty minute release and replacement. You are now going to release judgements, thoughts, emotions, behaviors and physical manifestations of blocked eleventh Chakra energy. Follow the chart below reading the *bolded italicized* words out loud after the statement.

Even if you believe you are not experiencing these issues
RELEASE anyway. Some one on the planet is
experiencing these issues. Do it for them.

*I release from my spiritual, mental, emotional, and
physical Body:*

I Can't Handle Life
Withdrawal
Shut Down
Shallow, listless, cold, impersonal, selfish
Problems with the hands or feet and the extremities

Take five deep breaths. Inhale through your nose and
exhale slowly through your nose five times. If your nose
is stopped up, then you may breathe through your mouth.
You may experience some lightheadedness, tingling or
yawning. These are signs of energy flowing.

Visualize the healing colors white and gold surrounding
your hands and feet. Breath deeply visualizing the breath
coming in and out through the palmar surface of your
hands and feet.

Speak the statement below out loud and say the ***bolded
italicized words*** out loud

*I take into my spiritual, mental, emotional, and
physical Body:*

"I fully participate in life's exchanges."

Five minute meditation: Sit quietly with your eyes
closed breathing normally. Slowly bring your awareness
back to your surroundings and open your eyes.

Observation During the Day

During your day pay attention to any judgements,
thoughts, emotions, behaviors and physical
manifestations related to the eleventh Chakra blockage.
Don't get caught up in them. Just note that they are
coming up. Breath your five count breath when they do
and speak your God conscious decision.

"I fully participate in life's exchanges."

Sit comfortably in a chair or on the floor to begin your second half hour session.

Five minute meditation: Visualize a spiral of pink energy in the palms of your hands and the soles of your feet. Bring the palms of your hands parallel to each other as if you are holding a ball six inches in diameter between your hands. Visualize and experience the energy passing back and fourth between your hands. Now bring your awareness to your feet. Stretch your legs out resting your feet on the heels so that the soles are not touching any surface. Visualize pink energy radiating from the soles of your feet. Breath deeply for twenty breathes during your visualization. Continue to breathe until you have completed twenty breathes through any images, thoughts, emotions, or physical sensations you experience.

Twenty minute release and replacement: Write down in your journal, using one or two word cues, any experiences you had during the day in which blocked eleventh Chakra judgements, thoughts, emotions, behaviors or physical manifestations were experienced. For example, note if you experienced feeling shut down, or withdrawn. Just write a cue word. Your subconscious has recorded the entire incident. It's on your subconscious tape. The cue word will bring forth the tape. Allow the one or two word associations with the experience to come forward. It may be the name of a person, situation, a color, etc. Don't get caught up with trying to grammatically word craft the cue word associations to the statement. Take 3 minutes and write out word association cues for all the times during the day you experienced personally or in relation to someone else, any judgement, thought, emotion, behavior and/or physical manifestation associated with a blocked eleventh Chakra. Read each association, repeat the statement below, filling each cue word into the blank space, one at a time, as you read the statement. You will repeat the entire statement each time as you fill in a different word cue. If you don't remember, or don't recognize that anything came up, that's fine. Just go back to page 132, and fill the **bolded italicized** words on the chart one at a time into the blank space of the statement below. Begin now.

This ....has no meaning to me I release and rise above that upset to a time and a place where it has no power over me.

Each time after reading the statement, take five deep breaths. Inhale through your nose and exhale slowly through your nose five times. If your nose is stopped up then you may breathe through your mouth. You may experience some light headedness, tingling or yawning. These are signs of energy flowing. Read the next word cue filling in the blank of the statement. Then take your breath. Repeat this process for the remainder of the twenty minutes or until you have released all the word cues you wrote down, whichever comes first. If you had no word cues and are using the chart from page 132, keep repeating the words on the chart until the twenty minutes are up. When you are finished repeat your God Conscious decision:

"I fully participate in life's exchanges"

Five minute meditation: Sit quietly with your eyes closed breathing normally. Slowly bring your awareness back to your surroundings and open your eyes.

Congratulations you have completed your journey. Acknowledge yourself for the commitment you have made and completed. Give your self nine days to integrate the subtle shifts that have taken place in your Body. Be gentle with yourself during this time and journal about your experiences. You have the opportunity to utilize the process again and again.

Addendum

These are suggestions of modalities you can use when processing and healing your Chakras. They can be used alone or in combination with each other.

1.Colors -- wear clothing or accessories with the healing colors for the Charka you are processing.

2. Eat foods that contain the colors or the healing colors of the Charka you are processing. In addition to the chart that I've constructed a more in depth reference is *Spiritual Nutrition and the Rainbow Diet* by Gabriel Cousens M.D. Dr. Cousens has constructed a diet in which foods are matched by color and vibrational harmony to the seven in-body Chakra. He also gives suggestions regarding the most appropriate times during the day to eat those foods.(see food chart)

Chakra	Chakra Color	Food	Healing Color	Food
First	orange/red	oranges, apples	white/pink	pears, grains
Second	red/green	tomatoes/greens	peach/violet	peaches/eggplant
Third	red/green/orange	red chard/carrots	yellow/gold/ruby	grains/raddicio
Fourth	golden	nuts/grains	pink	pink grapefruit
Fifth	blue/green	blue corn	blue	blueberries
Sixth	rose/purple/blue	rose hips	indigo/green	grapes
Seventh	yellow/violet	bananas/plums	violet	beets
Eighth	Mother of pearl	Light	white/gold	Light
Ninth	gold	Light	gold/white	Light
Tenth	earth tones	potatoes/kiwi	pink/peach	see above list
Eleventh	pink	pink grapefruit	white/gold	see above list

3. Work with the healing element for the Charka you are processing. For example, the healing element for the sixth Chakra is water. When processing the sixth Charka drink lots of water, bathe in water, surround yourself with bowls of water when you process.

4. Locate music containing the instruments indicated as healing for the Chakra you are processing and play it during the day as well as when you are processing.

5. Baths combine the power of water with the power of the ingredient placed in the water. The following essential oil baths were developed by and are contained in the book *Water Magic* by Mary Muryn. I have matched them to the appropriate Chakra. Essential oils do not dissolve easily in water they are best mixed with a vegetable oil, honey or cream (Muryn pg 31). This allows them to be dispersed by the water and absorbed by the skin. It is generally best to pour the oil mixture in after you have adjusted the water temperature and filled the tub.

Second Chakra bath (for women only)- take a handful of each of the following herbs (not the essential oils) and seep it like a tea in two quarts of boiled water for 20 minutes. Strain it with cheese cloth and pour into your bath water. Herbs: Sage, Thyme, Rosemary, and Whole cloves.

Third Chakra bath 10 drops of Lavender Oil and 10 drops of Lemon Oil.

Fourth Chakra bath 7 drops of Rose Oil and 3 drops of Lily of the Valley Oil.

Sixth Chakra bath 5 drops of Lilac Oil and 5 drops of Lemon Grass and 5 drops of Juniper Oil

Seventh Chakra bath 5 drops of Magnolia Oil and 5 drops of Juniper Oil.

Eighth Chakra bath 3 drops of Nutmeg Oil and 5 drops of Juniper Oil.

Ninth Chakra bath 5 drops of Mimosa Oil and 5 drops of Juniper Oil. Use as a night time bath and keep a pad and pencil at your bedside.

Tenth Chakra bath 1 lb. of baking soda and ½ lb of salt (sea salt is best but table salt or kosher salt will do)

Enjoy!

The Circle of Life

After reading this book and taking your journey, you have reached a different level of awareness. Your empowerment will continue to grow as you consciously utilize the knowledge you've gained about your Body and your Self. Each conscious decision to read the messages of your experiences and process yourself through them will take you through another energy cycle in the four directions.

You will face the North again and again. Your judgements and behavior will freeze assuming another form when they are thawed. You will find yourself again and again facing East, the rising Sun of consciousness lighting up and dissolving the shadows cast by judgements and fear. Again you will turn to the South for regeneration, remembering to embrace the three sisters Wisdom, Will and Love, who enable you to be responsible, stay on purpose, and allow Love to unfold. Facing the West again you will death miscreations in the fire of the setting sun arising to carry forth each new day in harmony with the present. May the energy of the four directions carry you to higher states of consciousness in the circle of life.

References

Bertalanffy, Ludwig von. <u>General Systems Theory</u>. New York: George Braziller, 1968.

Bonheim, Jalaja. <u>Aphrodite's Daughters</u>. New York: Simon and Schuster, 1997.

Byars, Rickie. "In The Land of I Am". Eternal Dance Music (BMI), 2000. (Audiotape.)

Chiprowassky, Madame. <u>Biotonic Therapy.</u>

Cousens, Gabriel. <u>Spiritual Nutrition and the Rainbow</u> Diet. Boulder, Co: Cassandra Press, 1986.

Dale, Cyndi. <u>New Chakra Healing</u>. St.Paul, MN: Llewellyn Publications,1998.

DeRohan, Ceanne. <u>Original Cause</u>. Santa Fe, NM: Four Winds Publications, 1986.

DeRohan, Ceanne. <u>Right Use of Will</u>. Santa Fe, NM: Four Winds Publications, 1986.

Dvorak, Jim. <u>The Chakra Thought Chart</u>. Santa Fe, NM: Body Light Seminars, 1988. (Chart)

Einstein, Albert. <u>Relativity </u>. Translated by Robert W. Lawson.15th ed. New York: Crown Publishers,1952

Foundation For Inner Peace. <u>A Course In Miracles</u>. Tiburon, CA: Foundation For Inner Peace, 1976.

Gerber, Richard. <u>Vibrational Medicine</u>. 3rd ed.Rochester, Vermont: Bear and Co, 2001.

Hay, Louise. <u>Heal Your Body</u>. 4th ed. Santa Monica, CA: Hay House, 1988.

Krauss, Lawrence M. <u>The Physics of Star Trek</u>. New York: Basic Books, 1995.

Kuthumy, Aeoliah. <u>Awakening Your Inner Light</u>. San Rafael, CA: Helios Publications, 1992.

Leadbeater, C.W. <u>The Chakras</u>. 8th ed. Wheaton, Il: Quest Books, 1997.

Muryn, Mary. Water Magic. New York: Simon and
Schuster, 1995.

Powell, A.E. The Etheric Double. 5th ed. Weaton, Il:
Quest Books, 1987.

Price, John Randolph. Practical Spirituality. Carlsbad,
CA: Hay House, 1985.

Raphaell, Katrina. Crystal Enlightenment. Santa Fe, NM:
Aurora Press, 1985.

Shapiro, Debbie. The Bodymind Workbook. Boston MA:
Element, 1991.

Walker, Dael. The Crystal Book. 12th ed. Sunol, CA:
1987.

Ywahoo, Dhyani. Voices of Our Ancestors.Boston:
Shambhala, 1987.

Zhang, Chan. "Dance of the Phoenix". Columbia, MD:
Chan Zhang, 1998. (Audiotape.)

Zukav, Gary. The Dancing Wu Li Masters. New York:
William Morrow and Company,1979.

ORDER FORM

SAVE YOURSELF
A Practical Guide to Understanding Energy, Emotions and Health

Help your friends, family and co-workers to "Save Themselves" by giving them a copy of this book. To order send $14.95 by money order, certified check or personal check. Add $4.00 for shipping and handling for single copies. ($19.95 total) Book will be shipped first class.

Quantity discounts are available as follows:

5 books	10% discount	remit	$ 67.28
10 books	15% discount	remit	$127,08
20 books	20% discount	remit	$236.00
30 books	25% discount	remit	$336.38
40 books	30% discount	remit	$418.60
50 books	35% discount	remit	$485.88

To get a quantity discount the following is applicable:
1. Discounts apply to five (5) or more copies.
2. All books must be sent to the same address.
3. Payment must accompany all orders. Please allow 3-4 weeks for delivery when paying by certified check or money order and 4-6 weeks when paying by personal check.
4. These discounts apply only to orders placed directly with us. Please do not ask for a discount   at your book store.
5. When ordering more than one book, add $1.00 for each additional book for shipping and   handling.

Make check or money order payable to:

Ebun Adelona
P.O. Box 156
Hot Springs, SD 57747-0156 USA

Ship to:

Name _____

Address _____

City _____

State _____

Zip_____ Country_____

Phone (   ) _____

Please send_____copies of **Save Yourself A Practical Guide
toEnergy, Emotions and Health** @ _____discount.

Subtotal $

_____

Shipping and Handling
$_____

South Dakota Residents add 4 % sales tax
$_____

Total Enclosed
$_____